HUMAN & SOCIAL BIOLOGY

artin Collins

, P.G.C.E., C.Biol., M.I.Biol.
d of Biology, Nailsea School, Bristol

lerie Wood-Robinson

., P.G.C.E., M.A.(ED), C. Biol., M.I. Biol.
cher Associate, Leeds National Curriculum
port Project
dren's Learning in Science Research Group,
ds University

Nelson Blackie

Thomas Nelson and Sons Ltd
Nelson House
Mayfield Road
Walton-on-Thames
Surrey KT12 5PL

Thomas Nelson Australia
102 Dodds Road
South Melbourne
Victoria 3205
Australia

First published by Thomas Nelson and sons Ltd 1993
© Martin Collins and Valerie Wood-Robinson 1993

Illustrated by David Gardner
Front cover courtesy of Ancient Art and Architecture Collection

ISBN 0-17-448200-0
NPN 9 8 7 6 5 4 3 2

ACKNOWLEDGEMENTS

The authors would like to acknowledge the help and support of colleagues, friends and
family, and the secretarial support of Gillian Porter and Maggie Pairaudeau

Photographic material:
Ancient Art and Architecture Collection 1, 17, 18; The Natural History Museum, London
2; Barnaby's Picture Library 3 (top and bottom), 27 (top left and right, bottom left and
right), 43, 76, 90; Science Photo Library 8 (left and right), 24, 35, 53, 68, 77, 102; Rex
Features 34; Bruce Coleman Limited 37, 72 (top left and right, bottom left and right); Alan
Cadogan 67; Wemer Forman Archive 43 (top left and right, bottom left and right); Museum
of London 80 (top); Health Education Council 81; *The Guardian* 86; Scottish Health
Education Group 101

The cover photograph shows a cave painting from the Nswaguti cave in Zimbabwe.
The painting depicts humans and a kuku (a large African antelope)

CONTENTS

General Editor's Introduction to the Series

Biology - Advanced Studies is a series of modular textbooks which are intended for students following advanced courses in biological subjects. The series offers the flexibility essential for working on modern syllabuses which often have core material and option topics. In particular, the books should be very useful for the new modular science courses which are emerging at A-Level.

In most of the titles in the series, one of the authors is a very experienced teacher (often also an examiner) and is sympathetic to the problems of learning at this level. The second author usually has research experience and is familiar with the subject at a higher level. In addition, several members of the writing team have been closely involved in the development of the latest syllabuses.

As with all text books, the reader may expect not to read from cover to cover but to study one topic at a time, or dip-in for information as needed. The index can be used like a science dictionary because where a page number is shown in bold print an explanation or definition will be found in the text. Where questions are asked, an attempt should be made at an answer because this type of *active reading* is the best way to develop an understanding of what is read.

We have referred throughout to *Biological nomenclature - Recommendations on terms, units and symbols*, Institute of Biology, London, 1989. We are delighted to be able to thank the many friends and colleagues who have helped with original ideas, the reading of drafts and the supply of illustrations.

Alan Cadogan
General Editor

Authors' Introduction to Human and Social Biology

In this book we have aimed to provide a basic content which is related to advanced syllabuses. At the same time it has been our intention to challenge you by incorporating a number of thought provoking questions in the text. Everyone is interested in the human condition, and the first chapter of this book is entitled 'What it is to be human'. The text is based firmly in the areas of biology and locating *Homo sapiens* within the animal kingdom, and we have endeavoured to identify how humans are a special and successful species of social animal. As you read this text, we hope that you will see the issues raised in relation to real people and recognise that the nature of human and social biology is its concern with these issues.

You will find ideas and data relating to many aspects of human life and human society - but perhaps more importantly, you will find questions that seek to promote discussion. It is important for you to offer your own ideas and to challenge and discuss the ideas of others. There are many questions - but for some, there is no single correct answer. 'Is the human population too great for the earth to support?', 'Is modern genetics interfering with natural laws?', 'What do we mean by equality?', 'Is research on the human embryo justified?', 'What is the role of the parent?'. Our responses to these and other questions help to create the values of human societies.

In challenging you to consider a number of different issues we have placed this book squarely in the real world. We hope that you, as the reader, will be stimulated to take some of the issues further and to find out for yourself 'what it means to be human'.

Martin Collins and Valerie Wood-Robinson

1

WHAT IT MEANS TO BE HUMAN

MYSTERY GIRL'S BODY DISCOVERED!

In a dried up lake, the remains of a young woman's body have been unearthed. While the remains were being pieced together, people nearby were playing a tape of their favourite music. The woman was named 'Lucy'.

But was she really a person and what was her real name? Why was only half of her skeleton found and was it a real skeleton?

Lucy was a small female australopithecine who lived three million years ago, beside a lake, in what is now Ethiopia. With forty per cent of her skeleton recovered she is the most complete specimen of an early hominid ever found. The shape of her pelvic bone shows that she was female, while the leg bones indicate that she walked upright. Her teeth suggest that she was about twenty years old when she died. The skeleton became famous under the name of 'Lucy' inspired by the Beatles' song 'Lucy in the Sky with Diamonds' (which was the music being played at the camp of the anthropologists shortly after the skeleton was found).

It is difficult to say whether 'Lucy' was a person or whether she was an ape. She was discovered in 1974 by Don Johanson and Tom Gray. After much consideration and comparison with other fossil remains, the scientists who discovered her gave her the species name *Australopithecus afarensis*, which means 'southern ape, found at Afar' (a place in north-east Ethiopia). Although she could walk upright she was not sufficiently like a human being to be given the genus name *Homo*, but her species is considered to belong to the *taxonomic* family, hominids. We can never know whether she had a personal name. We can never know whether she and her companions could speak or had the idea of personal identity.

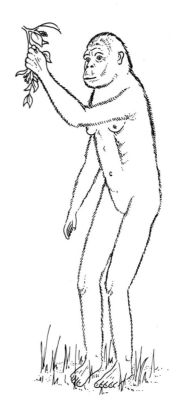

Figure 1.1 Did Lucy look like this?

At Afar, there are sedimentary rocks, 200 metres thick, formed from mud deposited by a now vanished lake. The joint Ethiopian, American and French anthropological team had been excavating there for several years. Previous to 1974, only parts of skulls and separate bones of such ancient hominids had been found at various sites in Africa. It was remarkable to find so much of one skeleton preserved over three million years. The skeleton was not made of the original bone, but was a fossil. The chemicals of the bone had been replaced by rock chemicals, retaining the structure of the bone and preserving it as rock.

■ CASE STUDY: THE EARLIEST HUMANS

Adam and Eve - The Fall of Man Engraving by Durer (1471-1528)

'And the LORD God formed man of the dust of the ground, and breathed into his nostrils the breath of life; and man became a living soul' (Genesis 2:7).
'And the rib, which the LORD God had taken from man, made he a woman, and brought her unto the man'
(Genesis 2:22)

Peking Man - *Homo erectus* from China

We have evidence that the Homo erectus people used fire, and we can imagine how this may have influenced their way of life. A fire would provide a centre for a permanent home base. People would gather round the fire, and so would tend to live in groups. Some members of the group would band together to go and hunt large animals. Others would gather seeds and fruits. Food would be brought back to the home base to be cooked and shared out amongst the members of the group.

Here are different artists' and writers' ideas about the earliest people. On your own, or in discussion with your colleagues work through these five questions:

 1. For each picture decide whether it is likely to be realistic and why you think that.

2. What do the phrases 'earliest humans', 'earliest people' and 'early Man' mean? What defines creatures as human?

3. From where or what did people originate? What evidence is there about the origins of humans?

4. How long ago did the earliest people live? What evidence do scientists have to date the earliest people?

5. What evidence is there to enable us to know about the appearance and lifestyle of early humans?

You probably find it difficult to answer these questions or to come to a consensus of agreement within your group. This chapter will help you to clarify some answers and to see why it is difficult for even the experts to reach an agreement about the origin of mankind.

■ DEFINING HUMANS

All human beings alive today and during the past are individuals of one species, *Homo sapiens* or Modern Man. This term, of course, includes the females of the species, so the term 'Man' is used correctly as the common name of the species, but the word 'human' or 'people' is often preferred as being less sexist. Modern people are different from other animals in several ways, not only in our body shape and appearance. We walk upright on two legs, we make tools including tools to make other tools, we harness the energy from fire and other natural resources, we communicate by speech, writing and other technologies, we have artistic and spiritual values and practices. We have an enormous brain to co-ordinate all of these activities and a correspondingly large skull to protect the brain.

■ Species, genus and family

Although people vary in their size, skin colour, facial features, blood groups and so on, these are variations within one species. The definition of a species is a group of individuals which can inter-breed to produce fertile offspring but which cannot interbreed with individuals of other species. A person can produce children with any other person (of the opposite sex!) but cannot breed with other animals to produce babies. The word species is both singular and plural.

Homo is a genus. A genus is a set of species which biologists put together because they are very similar in structure and way of life. There are no other living species sufficiently similar to humans to be grouped in the same genus, so the genus, *Homo* contains only one living species, *Homo sapiens*. Fossil evidence suggests that some creatures living in the past and now extinct were sufficiently like modern people to be considered as other species of *Homo*, that is, earlier kinds of Man.

Similar genera (plural of genus) are grouped together into a family. (This is a technical term in taxonomy, and should not be confused with the everyday sense of a family of individual people.) The family *Hominidae* includes the genus, *Homo*, and some extinct creatures, not quite human in structure but similar enough to be named as different genera of *hominids*. People are fascinated by apes in zoos and on films. This is because of their obvious similarity to us in their appearance and behaviour. Biologists consider the similarities

sufficient to group the family *Hominidae* with the family of apes (*Pongidae*) into the superfamily *Hominoidea*. Therefore the word *hominoid* refers to any ape-like or human-like creature.

■ Biological classification of Man

Most people, if asked whether they, or people in general, were animals, would be indignant and deny it. But, biologically, humans are animals. They are living things which move about, eat food and have cells whose structure and chemical functioning are like those of other animals.

Are humans 'animal'?

Are animals 'human'?

The classification of living animals gives some clues to the possible origins of the human species. In taxonomy, organisms are grouped according to their similarities. Scientists believe that these similarities are evidence of descent from common ancestors, with greater similarities indicating closer relationship.

Taxonomy is a human invention to make sense of the variety of natural life and to try to express supposed relationships. Biologists are not in total agreement on details of taxonomic categories. Therefore, you may find slightly different details in other books but the principles are the same.

Biological taxonomy is a hierarchical system. Each level is a universal set of mutually exclusive subsets, i.e. there is no intersection of subsets.

The specific name consists of two words, for example. *Homo sapiens*. It must be printed in italics or written underlined. Generic names must always begin with a capital letter (e.g. *Homo*), and specific epithets with a small letter (e.g. *sapiens*)

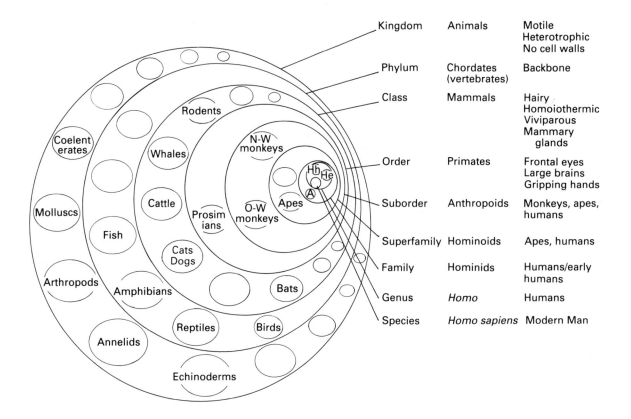

Kingdom	Animals	Motile Heterotrophic No cell walls
Phylum	Chordates (vertebrates)	Backbone
Class	Mammals	Hairy Homoiothermic Viviparous Mammary glands
Order	Primates	Frontal eyes Large brains Gripping hands
Suborder	Anthropoids	Monkeys, apes, humans
Superfamily	Hominoids	Apes, humans
Family	Hominids	Humans/early humans
Genus	*Homo*	Humans
Species	*Homo sapiens*	Modern Man

Figure 1.2 Man's place in the classification of animals.

In this diagram the subsets shown by small marginal circles are no less important, or numerically significant, than the large circles. The nesting circles representing the taxonomy of Man are shown large to fit in the information. In the diagram the names of the taxonomic groups are given as English plurals with lower case initials, e.g. animals, hominids. In the text they are sometimes given with Latin endings and capital initials, e.g. *Pongidae*, *Hominoidae*.

Tree-shrew

4 cm

Slow loris

5 cm

Ring-tailed lemur

9 cm

Figure 1.3 Some primates - prosimians

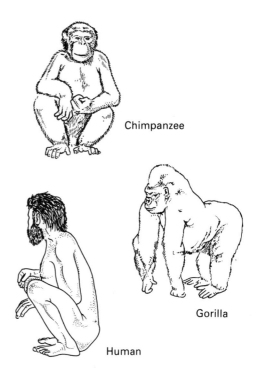

Chimpanzee

Gorilla

Human

Figure 1.4 Some primates - anthropoids

Humans, like all other animals with a backbone, are vertebrates (belonging to the phylum chordates). They are therefore related to all other vertebrates. Vertebrates are classified into five classes and humans belong to the class of mammals, being *homoiothermic* (of a constant body temperature) and hairy. Human babies, like those of other mammals, develop in the mother's uterus and feed on milk from her mammary glands. So humans are more closely related to other mammals, such as cats, than they are to frogs or fishes.

All mammals have some basic plan for their skeleton, teeth, circulatory system and other organs. The variations on these plans, related to their way of life, are used to divide mammals into about twenty orders. Whales and bats are orders which have their limbs specialised for swimming and flying respectively. Lemurs, monkeys and apes do not have specialised bodies or limbs for specific movement. Although there is no single, defined characteristic in common, they are grouped in the order *Primates*. Their unspecialised mammalian bodies with unspecialised limbs can

be used for a variety of purposes: climbing, swinging, running, jumping and even swimming. The five digits on primate limbs are mobile, especially the thumb or big toe which is opposable, allowing grasping. They have nails, rather than claws, and sensitive skin on the fingertips. These characteristics enable primates to sense and manipulate their environment with their hands and feet. Primates have four incisor teeth in both the upper and lower jaw and have forward-facing eyes which allow stereoscopic vision. They have efficient ears and a flexible neck which allows all-round vision and sound location. The sense of smell is less well-developed than in other mammals. The brain is well-developed with large areas to receive the input from eyes, ears, fingers and toes and to control the fine movement of the limbs. Most primates' babies are born singly and in a relatively helpless state, depending for a long time on care from the parents and family group. These characteristics are mostly adaptations for life in trees but they also apply to humans. We are therefore primates and assumed to be more closely related to other primates than to bats or whales.

The primates are divided into two suborders. The prosimians are tree-living primates. Tree-shrews do not look like primates, but like insectivores. These small animals have a pointed snout, eyes on the side, and teeth like insectivorous mammals. They scurry about in trees feeding on fruit and insects. They are classed within *Primates* because they have large eyes and a visual area of the brain, separate digits with the first slightly opposable, and skeletal details similar to primates. Lemurs, lorises and bushbabies have progressively more typical primate features in their eyes, faces, hands and reproductive patterns.

Most primates belong in the other suborder, the anthropoids. They have larger brains, more intelligent behaviour, more expressive flatter faces, and more mobile hands than prosimians. Within the anthropoids, apes and humans are separated from monkeys, into the hominoid superfamily, as mentioned above, sharing the characteristics o shoulder blades at the back (not the sides), lack o a tail, and Y-shaped patterns on the top of their molar teeth. So, on the evidence of similarities with living animals, humans are closely related to apes. Most biologists believe that apes and humans had a common ancestral species about 40 million years ago and long since extinct.

▮ Our closest living relatives
As well as anatomical similarities (see Fig.1.5), similarities in chromosomes and biochemical molecules can provide clues to relationships.

▮ Which is our closest relative?
Study Table 1.1 opposite, which shows some of the features of primates. It is not important for you to understand or learn the details of these features, but just use them as evidence to decide which species is Man's closest living relative.

▮ Possible family trees
Much of this evidence, and evidence from other features, is conflicting. Whatever you decide, you may well be right. The 'family tree' is probably like (c) rather than (a) or (b). Our closest living relatives are probably both chimpanzees and gorillas.

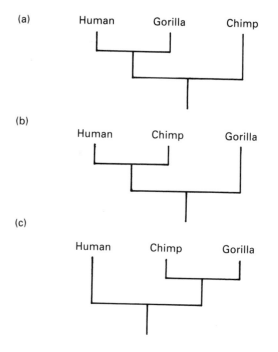

Figure 1.6 Possible family trees

Our modern 'cousins' can give us some ideas about our origins but they are not our ancestral types. Humans are *not* descended from monkeys or chimpanzees although both humans and chimpanzees probably had great, great, (500 000 times) grandparents in common about ten million years ago.

Hands

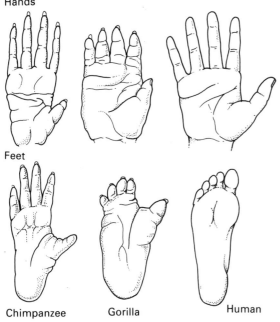
Feet

Chimpanzee   Gorilla   Human

Figure 1.5 Hands and feet of some primates

6

Feature \ Species	Gorilla	Human	Chimpanzee	Other primates
Frontal sinus in skull	Yes	Yes	Yes	No
Canine teeth	Large	Small	Large	Large
Number of chromosomes	48	46	48	42 or more
Chromosomes 5 and 12	Different from other primates	Like other primates	Different from other primates	
Fluorescence of chromosomes Y and 13	Same as human	Same as gorilla	Like other primates	
Haemoglobin	One amino acid different from human	Identical to chimpanzee	Identical to human	Different from human
Myoglobin	Like chimpanzee	Like other primates	Like gorilla	Like human

Table 1.1

■ FOSSIL EVIDENCE OF OUR EARLY PRIMATE RELATIVES

The oldest fossils with any primate characteristics were found in rocks in Europe and America about 70 million years old. These animals were promisians, not much different from squirrels (which are rodents, not primates) except in their teeth which resembled modern prosimians. For about 30 million years various kinds of prosimians evolved and then became extinct.

Fossilised fragments (teeth and jaws) of anthropoids, which are about 40 million years old, were found in Egypt. These ancient anthropoids were something like modern monkeys, living in the trees, where good vision, an elaborate communication and social life, mobile hands and single babies were advantages. The arboreal life may have produced the selection pressures for these characteristics of later primate groups, including the now extinct dryopithecine apes quite similar to modern chimpanzees.

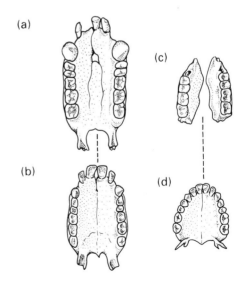

(a) (b) (c) (d)

Figure 1.7 Fossil fragments of (a) *Proconsul major*, a dryopithecine, show similar parallel rows of teeth as in the chimpanzee (b). Ramapithecus (c) was thought to be a fossil hominid as its teeth were in a curve similar to Modern Man (d)

■ Fossil hominids

Ramapithecus

In the 1930s fossil jaw fragments from ape-like creatures were found which dated back 14 million years ago. At the time of discovery they were thought to be the earliest hominids and were named Ramapithecus. Up until the 1970s and 1980s this opinion still held. Recent evidence, however, dismisses Ramapithecus as a direct human ancestor and places it in the Orang group. The search for early fossils continues!

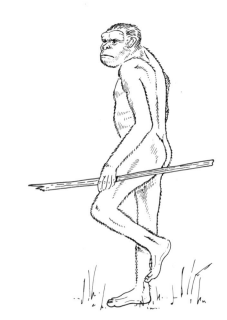

Figure 1.8 *Australopithecus*

A collection of bone fragments of *Ramapithecus*, an ancestor of the orang-utan

Australopithecus

In 1924 a fossilised skull of a child was found in a quarry at Taung in South Africa. It was the most ancient, fairly complete hominid skull yet discovered, at over a million years old. This child was different from both *Ramapithecus* and from humans. After much suspicion of its discoverer and much scientific debate, it was decided that this was a distinct species to be named *Australopithecus africanus* meaning the 'southern ape from Africa'. (The name has nothing to do with Australia; both words come from the Latin word for south.)

Since that discovery, the fossilised remains of several hundred australopithecines have been found in many parts of Africa, mainly along the Rift Valley. These hominids lived between 4 million and 1.5 million years ago.

Fossilised footprints from Tanzania dating from, 3.5 million years ago. These trails were fossilised in volcanic ash

Q 6. Look at the evidence in the photograph on page 8. How do you think these creatures stood and walked and ran?

7. What can you deduce about the creature that made these footprints? How many individuals were there? How did they walk?

8. Were they australopithecines? What can you tell about their family life?

There is considerable variation between the australopithecine skeletons that have been discovered, but they can be grouped into two types, the *gracile* and the *robust*.

The gracile australopithecines were slender and lightly built. They were about four feet tall and had rather protruding jaws. Their teeth were very like humans' and show that they probably ate meat. The typical *A. africanus* specimens are gracile, as is 'Lucy', who was given the species name *A. afarensis* (see Fig.1.8).

The robust australopithecines were much bulkier, about five feet tall and heavily built (*A. robustus*). Some had protruding ridges of bone above their eyes and ridges along the top of the skull. They had massive jaws and large molars which indicates that they were vegetarians, probably seed eaters. Some specimens have been given other species names, for example *A. boisei* (nutcracker man), but some people think this a subspecies *A. robustus boisei*. It is difficult to be sure of distinct species from fossil evidence. Could *A. robustus* breed with *A. boisei*, or even with *A. africanus*? It is impossible to apply this criterion of a species to populations long since extinct.

Were australopithecines *people*? Their skull size shows that their brains were chimpanzee-sized rather than human-sized. They may have used stones or bones as tools but there is no evidence that they made tools. Some crudely made stone tools were found near some australopithecine remains and at first it was thought that these creatures had made them, suggesting human status. Now it is thought that another kind of hominid, contemporary with *Australopithecus* three million years ago, made these tools.

How does *Australopithecus* fit into the family tree of humans? There is not enough evidence to be sure but here are some possibilities (see Fig 1.9).

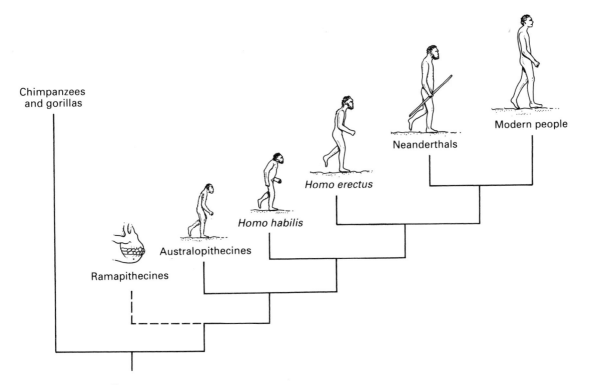

Figure 1.9 Family tree of humans

Whichever pattern is correct there appears to have been a division in the evolutionary line about 2.5 to 3 million years ago. Evidence from other fossilised animals found with the australopithecines suggests that the early gracile australopithecines lived in forested habitats where they could catch animals to eat. Then a climatic change occurred with the forest area becoming open savannah. The robust type then evolved which could survive in such conditions. Other hominids evolved which depended for survival in harsh conditions on their ability to manipulate their environment (e.g. by building shelters).

■ EARLY TOOL-MAKERS

An artefact may be defined as 'a product of human art and workmanship'. The oldest human artefacts have been found in East Africa. Some two million year old pebble tools were found at the Olduvai Gorge and were called 'Olduwan culture'. Then in 1972, older but better made implements were discovered at East Rudolf. At both sites,

australopithecines have been found, and also another fossil hominid named by its discoverer, Dr Louis Leakey, as Ho*mo habilis* meaning 'handy man'. This is the earliest creature to be assigned to the genus, *Homo*, that is, to be considered as human, on the basis of making tools. These creatures collected stones, often from miles away, and used other stones to shape them into tools to use as choppers, scrapers and knives. They must have been intelligent and co-operative, to solve problems by making tools. They were the first creatures to work for their survival by manipulating their environment. These early people (known as habilines) may have been living at East Rudolf three and a half million years ago and were certainly at Olduvai two million years ago, perhaps even earlier.

Homo habilis was about the same size as gracile australopithecines and walked similarly but had a bigger brain. *Homo habilis* is distinct from modern human beings in stature, face shape, brain size, and so on. Therefore it is classified as a distinct species of Man.

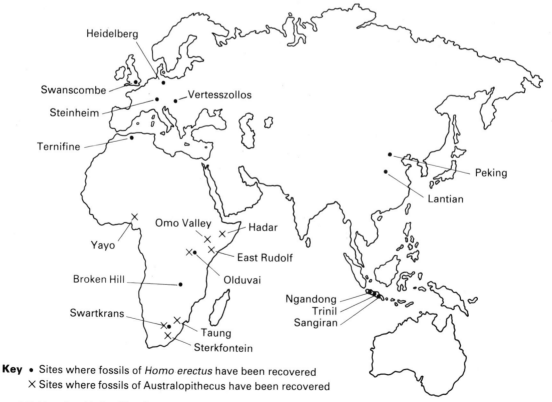

Key • Sites where fossils of *Homo erectus* have been recovered
✕ Sites where fossils of Australopithecus have been recovered

Figure 1.12 Map of world - fossil locations

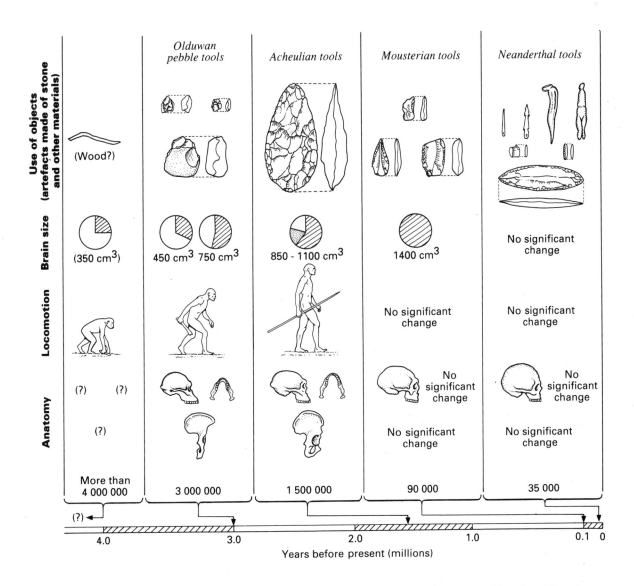

Use of objects (artefacts made of stone and other materials)		Olduwan pebble tools	Acheulian tools	Mousterian tools	Neanderthal tools

Use of objects (artefacts made of stone and other materials): (Wood?)

Brain size: (350 cm³) | 450 cm³ 750 cm³ | 850 - 1100 cm³ | 1400 cm³ | No significant change

Locomotion: | | | No significant change | No significant change

Anatomy: (?) (?) (?) | | | No significant change / No significant change | No significant change / No significant change

More than 4 000 000 | 3 000 000 | 1 500 000 | 90 000 | 35 000

(?)

Years before present (millions): 4.0   3.0   2.0   1.0   0.1   0

Figure 1.11 Human evolution, projected over a possible span of ten million years, begins at a slow pace when a still undiscovered hominid branches off from the hominoid stock ancestral to Man, the chimpanzee and the gorilla at some time more than four million years ago (far left). It is assumed that the ancestral hominid had a small brain and walked on its knuckles. This mode of locomotion enables a quadruped to move about while holding objects in its hands, leading to the further assumption that the hominid outdid living chimpanzees in manipulating sticks and other objects. By four million years ago the African fossil record reveals the presence of an advanced hominid: *Australopithecus*. This subhuman had a pelvis that allowed an upright posture and a bipedal gait. The size of the brain had increased to some 450 cm³. Stone tools soon appear in the archaeological record; they are simple implements made from pebbles and cobbles. The tools may have been made by a second hominid group, chiefly notable for having a much larger brain: 750 cm³. Next, about 1.5 million years ago, the first true Man, *Homo erectus*, appeared. Still primitive with respect to the morphology of its cranium and jaw,

H. erectus had an essentially modern pelvis and a striding gait. Its brain size approaches the modern average in a number of instances. Many stone tools that are contemporaneous with the fossils of *H. erectus* are 'cores' from which flakes have been removed on two sides; they are representative of the Acheulian tool industry. Not until some 100 000 years ago did *Homo sapiens* appear, in the form of Neanderthal man. The shape of Neanderthal's skull is not quite modern but the size of its brain is. Most of the tools found at Neanderthal sites represent the Mousterian industry; they are made from flakes of flint rather than cores. Only 40 000 years ago Modern Man, *Homo sapiens sapiens*, arrived on the scene. His skull is less robust than that of Neanderthal and his brain is slightly smaller. Many of his stone tools are slender blades; some, known as laurel-leaf points, appear to be ceremonial rather than utilitarian. Among his bone artefacts are needles, harpoon heads, awls and statuettes. About 10 000 years ago Man's transition from hunting to farming began.

■ Homo erectus

Other remains found as fossils in East and South Africa, Europe and Asia represent a group called *Homo erectus* (upright man). They lived more than a million years ago and became extinct about 150 000 years ago. They seem to be the first human inhabitants of Europe. The cave scene painting on page 2 shows what they may have been like.

They were about five feet tall (c.150 cm) and had larger brains than habilines, but smaller than modern people. Their skulls have low foreheads and massive brow ridges which are not on modern skulls. They were clearly *people* as their remains are often associated with evidence of cultural activities, such as well-made stone tools called Acheulian tools (see Fig.1.11).

A major milestone in human development was the domestication of fire. There is evidence that they used fire in Europe and Northern Asia, probably to keep warm in cold climates while living in caves and to cook their food. There is no way of knowing whether they had developed the human characteristic of speech. There was considerable variation within *Homo erectus* people, as there is within present-day people. We cannot be sure how distinct they were from *Homo sapiens*. We cannot know whether they were our direct ancestors or another branch of human evolution.

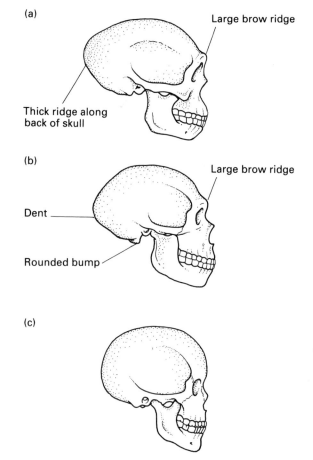

Figure 1.13 (a) *Homo erectus* skull, Peking Man, (b) Neanderthal skull from La Ferrassie, France, (c) modern human skull

■ The Neanderthals

The first discovery of a fossil human was made in 1856. As it was found in the Neander Valley in Germany it was named Neanderthal Man. Since then many similar fossils, some in groups of ten or more, have been found in Europe and the Middle East. Most of them lived between about 100 000 and 350 000 years ago, before and during the last ice age. Their skeletons are very similar to today's people and they were also about five feet tall. In general their teeth and jaws were stronger and they had more prominent brows and sloping foreheads. However, they are considered to be *Homo sapiens*, rather than *Homo erectus* or another species of Man. This is on the basis of their brain size and their culture and ceremonies. Neanderthals had an average brain size of nearly 1400 cm^3, almost identical to the average for living

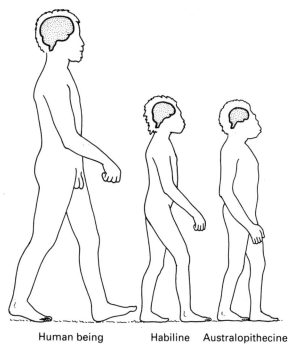

Human being   Habiline   Australopithecine

Figure 1.12 Brain sizes

people, compared to Homo ere*ctus* with a brain size of about 1000 cm^3. Such large brains imply a high level of intelligence which is reflected in the relics of Neanderthal culture. These people made stone implements of a particular advanced type called Mousterian tools (see Fig.1.11) and used these to butcher enormous animals, such as mammoths and rhinoceroses, which they trapped in pits. They also used fire.

Moreover, there is evidence that they must have held ceremonies for their dead. Neanderthal graves have been found with objects arranged in patterns and with signs of fire beside them. This suggests that these people had some sort of religious sense and possibly language to express abstract ideas. Neanderthals are clssified as a subspecies of Modern Man, *Homo sapiens neanderthalensis*.

■ Modern-type people

Neanderthals lived throughout Europe until about 35 000 years ago. Human fossils later than this are identical to modern people. Perhaps the modern-type people (*Homo sapiens sapiens*) evolved in Africa and moved to Europe. They were more adept at survival, and the Neanderthals who could not compete retreated northwards and died out. Or perhaps the modern people were descended from groups of Neanderthals which had become geographically separated and so were prevented from breeding with other Neanderthals. On the other hand there may have been complete interbreeding so the two types merged into one. Whatever their origin, by about 30 000 years ago, modern-type humans had spread to nearly all parts of the world, living in groups in the Old Stone Age or Palaeolithic cultures. One such culture, called the Cro-Magnon, has left evidence of their very human way of life. These people lived by hunting animals and gathering plants and they were organised into large social groups, probably dividing the work between them. They lived in caves, probably using them as temporary shelters. They must have used spoken language. They are the first people to leave evidence of art and symbolism.

■ RECENT EVOLUTION

The human species has not changed physically in the past 30 000 years, but culture has evolved since the time of Cro-Magnon people. This is described in the next chapter.

■ LIMITATIONS OF FOSSIL EVIDENCE

It is not possible to date fossils precisely. The evidence for evolution rarely consists of a complete series of fossils. Few primate fossils have been found and very few whole skeletons. Most evidence of human ancestors is derived from partial skulls. Cumulative evidence of trends in fossil types can give us negative information. For example the evidence that there were no humans on earth 100 million years ago is very powerful, as the only mammal fossils found from that time were tiny creatures like shrews. Likewise, it is fairly certain that there were no humans ten million years ago as no human fossils of that age have been found. The bones that are known from that time show a gradual, though sporadic, approach to the human condition. The earliest skull of a fully modern-type is of a person living only 40 000 years ago.

There is no direct evidence from the fossil record to give us such a detailed picture as shown of Lucy in Fig.1.1. However, anatomists studying skeletal remains can work out posture and gait. Teeth and jaws give evidence of diet and hence way of life. From the evidence the artist can fill in imaginative details.

The fossil record cannot give direct evidence of thought, behaviour, speech or interbreeding, that is, of the criteria which define the species *Homo sapiens*. So fossils cannot tell us directly when our species originated. The current story of evolution is tentative. It is constantly being revised as more evidence comes to light.

■ DATING OF FOSSILS

• *Principle of superposition.* The oldest layers of sedimentary rocks and hence the oldest fossils are at the bottom and the newer ones are above. This gives a sequence of fossils.
• *Fluorine content measurements* of a fossil and the deposits around it can give a relative age.
• *Potassium-argon estimation.* The proportion of these two elements in a sample varies with its age and can help to put an absolute age on fossils from different places.
• *Carbon-14 estimation.* The amount of this radio-active isotope (^{14}C) in a sample of carbonaceous material decreases with its age. It is used to give absolute dates to specimens up to 50 000 years old.

PEOPLE IN SOCIETY

A FLORAL FUNERAL

There is a large cave in the Zagros mountains of northern Iraq called the Shanidar cave. A man, woman and child were found buried in one grave in the cleft of a rock. The remains of six species of wild flowers were found in the grave, carefully arranged, especially around the man's body. These had been beautiful yellow, white and blue flowers with herbal properties. The people had been buried in late spring, but of which year? Judging from the rock layers in which the burial was found, if you choose any year between 60 000 and 40 000 years ago, you could be right!

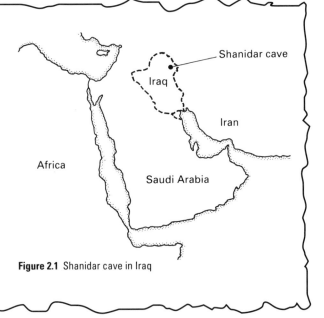

Figure 2.1 Shanidar cave in Iraq

Ralph Solecki (an American anthropologist and archaeologist) and his team excavated in the area of the Shanidar cave for more than twenty years. From the evidence of the grave, he was able to deduce a lot about the people found. They were decidedly human, probably a family of father, mother and child. They had friends and relations, that is, they lived in a social group, as they had been carefully buried. Other graves nearby contained skeletons showing signs of injury or disease during the lifetime of the people. This indicates that the community cared for its disabled members.

The plant remains in the grave consisted of pollen. This was carefully collected from different parts of the grave and analysed by Arlette Leroi in Paris. She identified the species of wild flowers that the pollen had come from, and hence the colour and herbal properties of the grave decorations. It also enabled her to identify the season of the burial. It showed that this was not a chance burial or mere disposal of rotting flesh, but that the society had rituals associated with death. The people must have been able to speak in order to communicate the complicated ideas involved in a caring and ritualistic society.

Physically the people were slightly different from the average modern person. They are regarded as a different subspecies of human beings called *Homo sapiens neanderthalensis* or Neanderthal Man.

The Shanidar cave had obviously been a good place to live for a considerable time, for there is evidence from the upper levels that other people occupied it much later - about 10 000 years ago.

(b)

Figure 2.2 (a) The rounded horn of a wild goat, (b) the flattened horn of a domesticated goat

These other people were indistinguishable in their skeletons from modern people; they were *Homo sapiens sapiens*, the same as us. Near by, at Zawi Chemi there were the remains of a human settlement with more skeletons of modern type people, dating from about 10 000 years ago. Stores of wheat, peas, acorns and pistachio nuts were found, as well as assorted bones of pigs, goats and other animals of various ages. The goats' horns were round in cross section, like those of wild goats (see Fig.2.2). However, Rose Solecki found a large number of sheep remains, 60 per cent of which were year-old lambs. Pig, goat and sheep bones were found in rubbish dump piles of odd bones. However, dogs were found as complete skeletons - and they were different from those of the wild wolves.

At Jarmo, another site in Iraq, there is evidence of a community of about 200 inhabitants, living about 8500 years ago. Amongst their remains, archaeologists have found goats' horns with *flat* cross sections, barley and wheat seeds unlike wild grasses, pottery, stone bowls and grindstones.

These excavations, and several others, help us to trace the story of human society in its early development.

■ THE SPREAD OF THE HUMAN POPULATION

The world-wide climatic changes at the end of the last ice age, about 10 000 years ago, enabled humans to spread out and colonise the whole world except Antarctica. Evidence from northern Europe suggests that people were concentrated into small groups, often along rivers, where they fished and hunted small animals and gathered wild plants to eat. Some made canoes and sledges, and some lived in tents they made of branches, bark and skins. We cannot tell whether these were temporary camps of nomads, moving from place to place following their prey, or whether they were more permanent homes. This period of human history is called the Mesolithic or Middle Stone Age.

■ THE FIRST FARMERS

The first evidence of growing crops and domesticated animals dates from about 9000 years ago. Agriculture leads to a settled lifestyle. It made an enormous change in the development of human society; this change is called the first agricultural revolution or the Neolithic revolution. Neolithic means New Stone Age. The first farmers lived in the Middle East, in a region called the Fertile Crescent. This is in what is now parts of Iran, Iraq, Turkey and Palestine. The ancestral varieties of the world's barley, wheat, sheep, goats, and pigs still exist in this region (see Fig.2.3).

■ The origin of farming

The hunter-gatherer lifestyle probably developed into the agricultural lifestyle by accident. In some places people harvested wild plants with stone sickles, and saved seeds from wild plants for winter feeding. Probably some of the seeds were spilt and germinated near the people's encampments. This gave them the idea of planting wild seeds and cultivating the plants as crops. Barley and emmer wheat were the earliest crops. Some Neolithic communities grew peas.

Once a community had settled in one place, with a steady supply of grain growing at the settlement, they would have tethered some small wild animals as a walking food store. This then led to the domestication of animals.

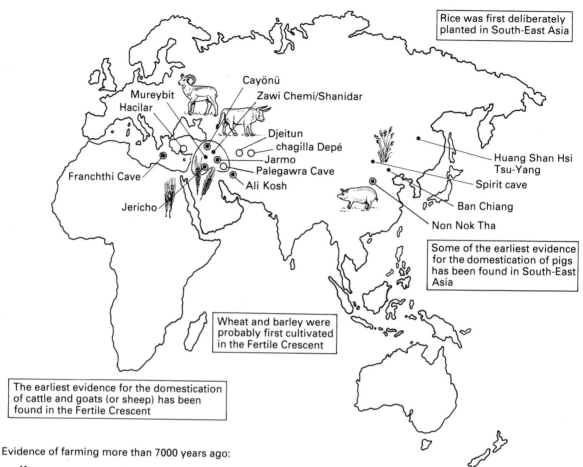

Rice was first deliberately planted in South-East Asia

Cayönü
Zawi Chemi/Shanidar
Mureybit
Hacilar
Djeitun
chagilla Depé
Jarmo
Palegawra Cave
Franchthi Cave
Ali Kosh
Jericho

Huang Shan Hsi Tsu-Yang
Spirit cave
Ban Chiang
Non Nok Tha

Some of the earliest evidence for the domestication of pigs has been found in South-East Asia

Wheat and barley were probably first cultivated in the Fertile Crescent

The earliest evidence for the domestication of cattle and goats (or sheep) has been found in the Fertile Crescent

Evidence of farming more than 7000 years ago:

Key
- • Cultivated plants
- ○ Domesticated animals
- ⌒ Fertile crescent

Figure 2.3 The development of farming

Q 1. Which type of animals did people domesticate first? Why did they choose these animals?

2. What two pieces of evidence from Zawi Chemi suggest that sheep were domesticated before goats?

3. Do you think that the people in Zawi Chemi ate dogs or kept them as workers or pets? What evidence supports your answer?

From 9000 to 5000 years ago the Neolithic culture spread north over Europe. People migrated and intermixed with the existing hunting populations, and took with them their ideas about agriculture. As they needed more land to grow crops, the early European farmers began to deforest the continent by cutting and burning trees. Separate agricultural revolutions appear to have occurred: one about 6000 years ago in South-East Asia, with the cultivation of rice and another in Mexico, with the cultivation of maize. The dense tropical forest areas prevented the rapid spread of agriculture throughout America and confined it to the valleys and coasts below the Andes, where subsequently civilisations developed.

■ URBANISATION

As people adopted the settled lifestyle enabled by agriculture, they built houses from mud, timber or other local materials. Their communities became organised into villages. The more secure way of life led to a population explosion. Some villages grew into towns. Excavations show that a settlement of about 2000 people existed at Jericho as long as 9000 years ago.

In time, great civilisations arose in the fertile regions where agriculture had originated. The first urban civilisation was that of Sumeria in the Tigris and Euphrates valleys about 6500 years ago.

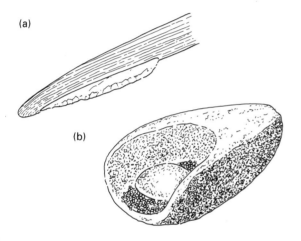

Implements from Jericho: (a) a small sickle (reconstructed) for cutting corn, the 'blade' of which is made of flint, (b) a grindstone for corn. Similar stones are still in use today in some countries

■ THE DISCOVERY OF METALLURGY

Around 6000 years ago, metallurgy began. Some Neolithic people discovered how to smelt copper and lead and they used these metals for making beads and ornaments. The discovery of adding tin to copper provided a new material, bronze, which was more versatile. It was used to make not only jewellery but tools and weapons superior to stone implements. This brought to an end the Stone Age in some parts of the world and by 5000 years ago the Bronze Age was established. Social organisation and technology gave rise to a number of city states led by kings with their armies fighting for territory and wealth in the Fertile Crescent region. The Babylonian civilisation united several of these city states around 4000 years ago.

■ COMMUNICATION

The more complex a social organisation becomes the greater the need is for an efficient communication system. We cannot know when people first acquired spoken language but it was certainly well before 10 000 years ago and may even have been 100 000 years ago. Language allows people to plan how to work co-operatively and enables information to be passed to different people in one generation and from one generation to another. Although Palaeolithic people communicated by drawing, the earliest known writing is on Sumerian stone tablets of 5500 years ago.

Sumerian writing on a stone tablet

Written language enables a store of information which can be communicated between people separated by great distances of space and time. Language, spoken and written, was a necessary tool for all other cultural developments that make humans so different from other animals.

■ AESTHETIC AND SPIRITUAL CULTURE

Art and religion are two aspects of culture which identify their originators as truly human. The earliest indication of some religious sense comes from evidence of ceremonies at Neanderthal graves, perhaps 50 000 years ago (see page 14). Graves of Palaeolithic people from 30 000 years ago indicate burial customs that varied at different places and times. The bodies have been found deliberately positioned and often covered in red ochre pigment.

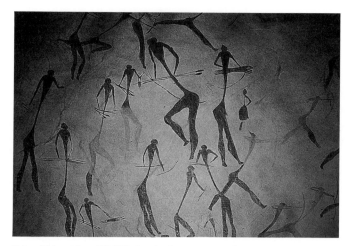

Palaeolithic art from 6000 BC showing hunters or warriors

Remains of shell and bone jewellery and of fur clothing have been found at some sites. Cro-Magnon people buried cave-bear skeletons in special arrangements as if these animals had some ritualistic significance.

We do not know when people first expressed themselves in art, but by 20 000 years ago our *Homo sapiens* ancestors in Europe were producing massive paintings on the walls of deep caves. They may have painted on exposed rock surfaces but only the paintings of mammoths, bison, horses and other animals on the walls of caves have been preserved. Beautiful carvings in bone, ivory and stone of animals and women have also been found, dating from about 20 000 to 10 000 years ago.

At this time much of Europe was covered by ice and the hunting people were compressed into small areas with limited supplies of prey. Many authorities think that the symbolic art was for magical, ritual or religious purposes to ensure successful hunting. Whistles made from animal bones have been found, indicating some musical activities which may have been of ritual significance, or for communication, or perhaps just for fun.

The Mesolithic hunter-gatherers and the Neolithic farmers have left little evidence of art or religion. Perhaps with more continuous food supplies to attend to they had neither the time nor the need to indulge in ritual art. As civilisations developed, religions became established with rituals and temples devoted to them. Art was used to adorn temples, palaces and people. The division of labour, necessary as society developed, included professional priests and artists, as well as soldiers and administrators - all of whom were dependent on the food-producing farmers.

HUMAN POPULATIONS

■ THE POPULATION BOMB

'While you are reading these words four people, most of them children, will die of starvation - and twenty four more babies will have been born.'

These words appeared on the cover of a book by Dr Paul Ehrlich in 1972. The words and the title of the book, *The Population Bomb*, were designed to focus our attention on a concern first expressed almost 200 years earlier. Thomas Malthus, in his *Essay on the Principle of Population* (1798), concluded that population would always outrun the supply of the necessities of life, particularly food. A section of his *Essay* is shown below.

Reading the passage below, It would be difficult to deny the truth of Malthus' two *postulata*:
... that food is necessary to the existence of man.
... that the passion between the sexes is necessary.
and perhaps few would wish to!

Q 1. What did Malthus consider would be the consequence of these two *postulata*?

2. What is the difference between a geometrical ratio and an arithmetical ratio?

"I think I may fairly make two postulata.

First, that food is necessary to the existence of man.
Secondly, that the passion between the sexes is necessary and will remain nearly in its present state.

These two laws, ever since we have had any knowledge of mankind, appear to have been fixed laws of our nature, and, as we have not hitherto seen any alteration in them, we have no right to conclude that they will ever cease to be what they now are without an immediate act of power in that Being who first arranged the system of the universe, and for the advantage of his creatures, still executes, according the fixed laws, all its various operations...

...Assuming then, my postulata as granted, I say that the power of population is indefinitely greater than the power in the earth to produce subsistence for man.
Population, when unchecked, increases in a geometrical ratio. Subsistence increases only in an arithmetical ratio. A slight acquaintance with numbers will show the immensity of the first power in comparison of the second.
By that law of our nature which makes food necessary to the life of man, the effects of these two unequal powers must be kept equal.
This implies a strong and constantly operating check on population from the difficulty of subsistence. This difficulty must fall somewhere and must necessarily be severely felt by a large portion of mankind.

There are many, however, who have questioned the conclusions which Malthus considered inevitable. They thought that there would always be enough food to support the human population. For a time their views seemed to be supported by the increases in productivity brought about by the Industrial Revolution and, more recently, by the Green Revolution. Perhaps human ingenuity could prove Malthus wrong.

By the late 1960s, however, the increased productivity began to look rather more like a temporary respite. Today, despite minor changes of detail, Ehrlich's message remains unchanged. The spectre of famine is all too familiar to us. Human population is still set to double in 40 years.

Scientists have established some general principles of populations in species other than humans. A *population* is a group of individual members of a species within a community. Knowledge of the number of individuals in the group (the population size) and the way in which it changes (population dynamics) is important in understanding and explaining what is happening in a community.

Whether a population increases, stays the same, or decreases, depends upon the balance between four factors, **birth rate (br), death rate (dr), immigration rate (ir)** and **emigration rate (er).**

Q 3. What is the simplest equation which can be written, using all of the above symbols, to express the population dynamics of a constant population size? (Answer on page 33.)

If a few individuals of a species are introduced into a new area in which conditions are favourable, e.g. rabbits on an offshore island, or greenfly on a rose bush, the growth of the population follows a well-defined pattern, i.e. the population growth curve (see Fig.3.1).

This S-shaped (sigmoid) curve is characteristic of growth in all living systems, in individual organisms as well as in populations. It consists of four distinct phases indicated by four different patterns of population change.

Phase 1: (sometimes referred to as the lag phase) shows the population growing slowly with a slow, but gradually increasing, rate of growth.

Q 4. How could the slow rate of growth be caused by the small number of individuals at the start of phase 1?

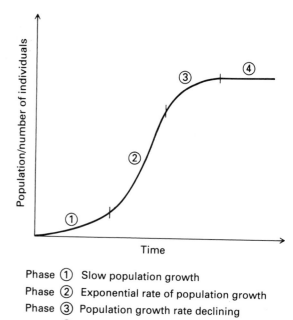

Phase ① Slow population growth
Phase ② Exponential rate of population growth
Phase ③ Population growth rate declining
Phase ④ Stable population

Figure 3.1 A generalised graph showing population growth with time. The rate of growth at any point is indicated by the slope of the curve - the steeper the slope the greater the growth rate

Phase 2: (the exponential phase) shows the population doubling for each unit of time (**generation time**) i.e. increasing geometrically. During this phase of growth the growth rate at its maximum.

Q 5. If, at the start of phase 2, a population contained twenty individuals and the phase lasted for six generation times, what would the population be at the end of the phase?

---

birth rate (br) the rate at which individuals are born

death rate (dr) the rate at which individual die

immigration rate (ir) the rate at which new individuals enter the community from outside

emigration rate (er) the rate at which individuals leave the community

generation time the time period between an organism being born and it producing offspring

---

From the answer to question 5 you can perhaps appreciate the potential of a single aphid to produce 6000 million offspring in a season or of a single bacterium to produce a mass of bacteria greater than that of the Earth in three days!! Of course this situation is never reached. The events of phase 3 show why.

Phase 3: shows population increasing more slowly and growth rate declining. If you have found an answer to the last question you will not be surprised to learn that the 64-fold increase in the population is beginning to stretch the resources of the environment to support it. Environmental resistance has set in causing a decreasing birth rate, an increasing death rate or both.

Q 6. What forms might environmental resistance take that would result in:
a) increasing death rate?
b) decreasing birth rate?

Phase 4: shows a constant or stable population and a *zero growth rate*. At this point a limit has been imposed by environmental resistance and an equilibrium has been reached between birth rate and death rate. (The term ZPG is also used for zero population growth, i.e. a stable population.)

The generalised growth curve is a useful model but it has limitations. The preceding explanation, for example, takes no account of immigration and emigration. In normal circumstances, these will have little or no influence on the population of a particular community but occasionally conditions and events may make their effects significant.

Q 7. What events could cause immigration or emigration on a significant scale in the non-human communities?

A further limitation of the generalised growth curve in Fig.3.1 is that it implies that once a population reaches equilibrium it remains constant, apparently for the foreseeable future. This is not usually so.
The factors which contribute to environmental resistance are both variable in strength and imprecise in their effects. In general terms

environmental resistance can be considered to be the result of the interaction between four factors:

• Availability of raw materials, i.e. food, water and oxygen. Abundance of food varies with climatic and soil conditions as well as with how much competition there is for the food.

• Presence or absence of disease and parasites. This varies markedly with the degree of over-crowding in the community.

• Availability of living space. This affects not only homes, shelter and territories but also the potential build up of poisonous wastes, the ease of the spread of disease and even the breeding potential of individual organisms.

• Presence or absence of predators.

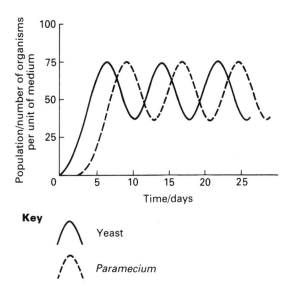

Key

Yeast

Paramecium

Figure 3.2 The effect of predation and food supply on population size. A nutrient medium was maintained at a constant temperature and at the start of the experiment (day 1) a culture of yeast cells was added. By regular sampling, the changes in the two populations were recorded and graphed

Q 8. In Figure 3.2 which is the predator and which the prey? How can you explain the shape of the population curves for prey and for predator over the first ten days of the experiment?

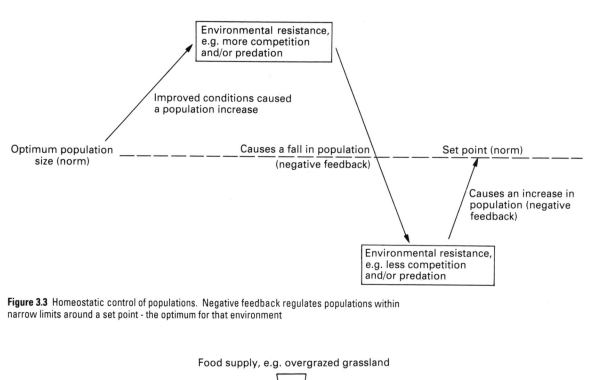

Figure 3.3 Homeostatic control of populations. Negative feedback regulates populations within narrow limits around a set point - the optimum for that environment

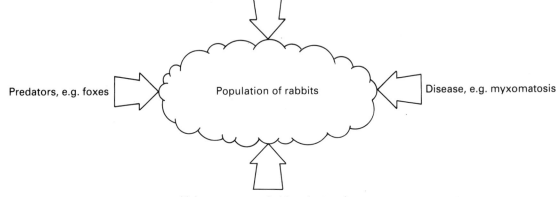

Figure 3.4 A scheme showing the influence of generalised factors of environmental resistance on population size

Figure 3.2 shows that the stabilisation of a population actually involves regular fluctuations above and below the optimum population for the particular environmental conditions. This illustrates too that population control is an example of negative feedback. This principle is outlined in Fig.3.3.

Schematically the regulation of the population of any species can be represented as shown in Fig.3.4.

Although there are no conclusive data available it seems likely that the populations of our pre-human ancestors were subject to this natural regulatory mechanism. Indeed, the limited data available for our own species in Britain up to as recently as the Roman invasion in 55 BC, suggests that the population was maintained at a fairly constant level for some 5000 years.

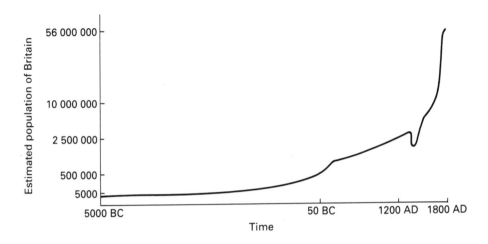

Figure 3.5 Human population changes in Britain since 5000 BC

However, as data becomes more reliable and the story is brought up-to-date it is clear from Fig.3.5 that something different is happening.

Q 9. What can you learn from the overall shape of the graph in Fig. 3.5?

10. What was happening in Britain in the fourteenth century to account for the shape of the population curve at that time?

Such local and short-term fluctuations cannot distract us from the trend shown by this and by world population figures (Table 3.1). The rapid increase in the human population since 1650 reflects certain well-documented population explosions in other species.

Date	Estimated world population (millions)
8000 BC	5
1650 AD	500
1850 AD	1000 (1 billion)
1930 AD	2000 (2 billion)
1975 AD	4000 (4 billion)
2000 AD	8000 (8 billion)

Table 3.1

In the case of the deer population illustrated in Table 3.2, the increase in the number of deer was caused by the extermination of many of its predators by hunters in 1907. This decreased the environmental resistance and created a different population with a higher norm (see Fig. 3.4). Thus, the deer population increased until another factor in the environment provided the environmental resistance. In this case it turned out to be the food supply. After 1925 mass starvation and death reduced the deer population to a new, lower norm or *set point*.

Date	Estimated deer population
1905 AD	4000
1925 AD	100 000
1930 AD	40 000

Table 3.2

Q 11. Do you think that there are any parallels which can be recognised in the patterns of deer population growth and human population growth?

Your answer to this question will be based on some direct evidence and some use of your imagination and guesswork to assemble circumstantial evidence. Making informed guesses and imagining outcomes is what we call speculation and it is an important mental tool for the scientist.

Q 12. What would you consider to be direct evidence and what is circumstantial evidence of population change?

23

Any answer is complex, because, even with the simplified model proposed to represent the regulation of population, there are four regulatory factors which might be removed or restricted in their influences.

Each of us has knowledge on which to base speculations about how new set points for the human population might have been established. This knowledge has been provided by historians, archaeologists and anthropologists.

Before we use such knowledge to aid our speculations we have to recognise a major difference between ourselves and other animals and plants. We have the ability to make significant changes to our environment. So, whereas other forms of life and their populations are subject to environmental change, our own species has the capacity to direct environmental change. This capacity does not give us *mastery* over our world - as natural disasters constantly remind us. Nor is it always wisely used - as Man-made disasters testify. It is, however, a unique ability and one that can be seen at work in profoundly influencing the human population.

Think about the four regulatory factors, i.e. birth rate, death rate, immigration rate and emigration rate, as they relate to the human population. You may wish to refer back to Chapter 2 to answer the following questions.

Q 13. Predation by wild animals is clearly no longer a regulator of the human population although our very earliest hominid ancestors presumably did not have things so easy! How were the effects of predation eliminated and when did this happen?

14. Famine throughout human history has caused untold misery. However, it has had little effect on world population change since events which began about 9000 years ago and spread more or less world-wide over the next 4000 years. What was it that began from that time to restrict the influence of food supply on human population growth?

15. Disease must seem to us an unlikely regulator of human population growth. It would be foolish to underestimate the destructive power of disease, even today, but the people of England in 1348

Human control of disease: an illustration of Edward Jenner showing him transferring cowpox scratches on the skin of a boy. Until the beginning of the 19th century, smallpox was one of the most dreaded diseases resulting in death in one in three cases. In 1827, Jenner innoculated his first patient with his new vaccine

would have needed no such warning. They saw almost one third of their number killed by the Black Death in that year. What has removed the spectre of disease from the human population equation?

16. 'Living space' has probably never been a serious constraint on human population growth on a world scale, at least not since our ancestors were hunter-gatherers. Some 'local difficulties' may have arisen but human inventiveness and adaptability has allowed our species to keep pace with the demands for more space. In what ways has this been achieved?

Your views on these questions will be wide-ranging but will almost certainly combine to provide an intriguing perspective on human cultural evolution previously discussed in Chapter 2. You might like to assign your ideas to a position on the chronological chart presented in Fig.3.6.

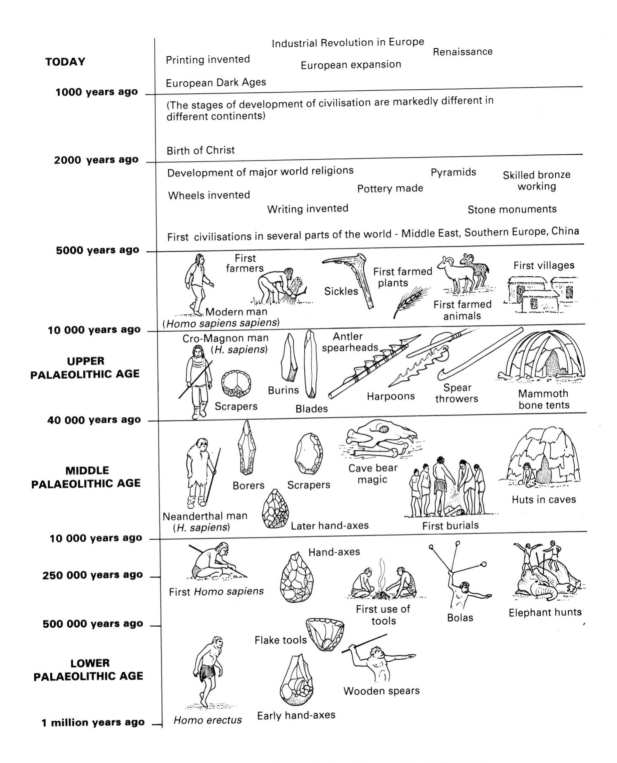

TODAY

Industrial Revolution in Europe

Printing invented   Renaissance

European expansion

European Dark Ages

1000 years ago

(The stages of development of civilisation are markedly different in different continents)

2000 years ago   Birth of Christ

Development of major world religions   Pyramids   Skilled bronze working

Wheels invented   Pottery made

Writing invented   Stone monuments

First civilisations in several parts of the world - Middle East, Southern Europe, China

5000 years ago

First farmers   First farmed plants   First villages

Sickles

First farmed animals

Modern man (*Homo sapiens sapiens*)

10 000 years ago

Cro-Magnon man (*H. sapiens*)   Antler spearheads

UPPER PALAEOLITHIC AGE

Burins   Harpoons   Spear throwers   Mammoth bone tents

Scrapers   Blades

40 000 years ago

MIDDLE PALAEOLITHIC AGE

Cave bear magic

Borers   Scrapers

Huts in caves

Neanderthal man (*H. sapiens*)   Later hand-axes   First burials

10 000 years ago

250 000 years ago

Hand-axes

First *Homo sapiens*

First use of tools   Bolas   Elephant hunts

500 000 years ago

Flake tools

LOWER PALAEOLITHIC AGE

Wooden spears

1 million years ago   *Homo erectus*   Early hand-axes

Figure 3.6 A chronology of some important developments in human cultural evolution over the last million years

In answering the questions on page 24 you have probably identified three cultural revolutions.

The *tool-making revolution* probably began as an aid to hunting (and presumably to defend against predators), as well as to aid domestic crafts associated with hunting. In one sense this revolution has continued to the present day although it has been incorporated into other broader revolutions including the discovery of metallurgy.

The *agricultural revolution* marked the transition from the hunter-gatherer culture to one based on settlement, the cultivation of crops and a more direct control over food supply. This revolution too has continued to the present day, in recent times being expressed as the Green Revolution of the 1960s.

The so-called *industrial revolution* may be better called the scientific revolution. It is based upon great advances in scientific discovery, invention and understanding with a much broader application than to just the technology of mass-production. In particular, it represents the first major human assault on disease (see Fig.3.7).

Each revolution represents a profound change in the human condition. In the current context each can be considered a change for the better as each represents an improvement in our control over environmental resistance. As such it follows that each is also likely to have contributed to a shifting of the set point of optimum human population. Is there any evidence to support this?

The only direct evidence we have is for the effects of the scientific revolution, the start of which is generally dated around the middle of the eighteenth century. This is also the start of the population explosion in which we now find ourselves.

Q 17. Two other population explosions dated around 6000 years ago and 20 000 years ago are suggested by archaeological evidence. How do these match up with the agricultural and tool-making revolutions?

One purpose of a model is to provide a framework into which we can insert current understanding and knowledge in order to predict outcomes and plan strategies. Bearing this in mind, consider whether the model in Fig.3.8 offers any insight. You could discuss this with your colleagues.

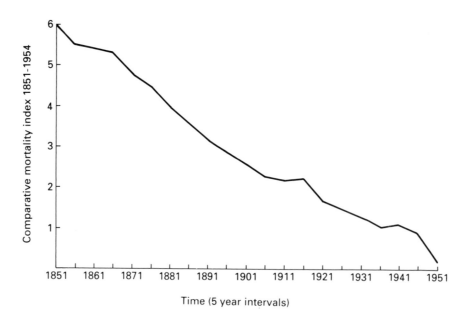

Figure 3.7 The human assault on infectious disease - the effect of improved living conditions and of immunisation on respiratory tuberculosis in England and Wales

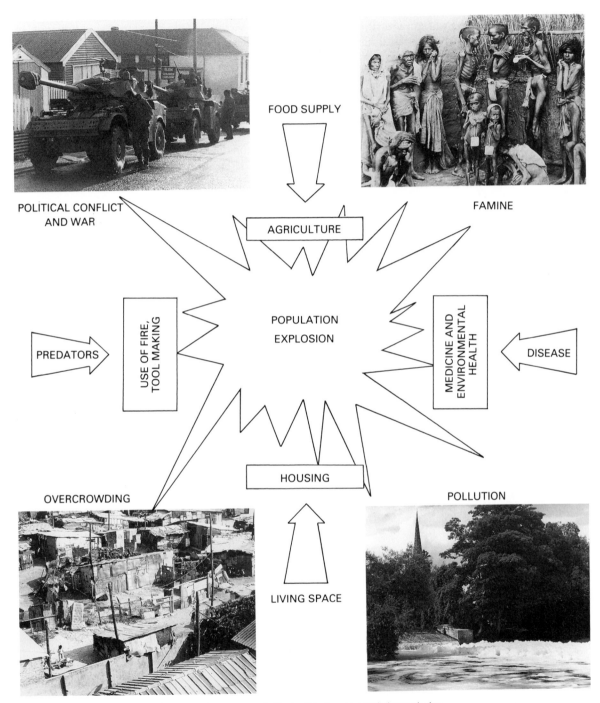

POLITICAL CONFLICT
AND WAR

FOOD SUPPLY

FAMINE

AGRICULTURE

PREDATORS

USE OF FIRE,
TOOL MAKING

POPULATION
EXPLOSION

MEDICINE AND
ENVIRONMENTAL
HEALTH

DISEASE

OVERCROWDING

HOUSING

POLLUTION

LIVING SPACE

Figure 3.8 A model of relationships between the causes and effects of the human population explosion

Your ideas on the model shown in Fig.3.8 may differ from those of your friends and you may recognise the limitations of its oversimplification. In particular, the interaction between factors and between consequences is not shown in this model. For example the use of inorganic fertilisers by modern agriculture as a means of providing more food has created a serious problem of pollution in water. There are many such examples but this one has been chosen because it also highlights another, more important oversimplification which needs explaining.

The debate as to whether or not the world is overpopulated has gone on for many years. In our model, overpopulation is implied and placed centrally as the apparent origin of many of the world's problems. Some people believe that an ideal world could support far more people than the 5 000 000 000 who, in some sense, overpopulate the real world now. The evidence for this 'over-population' comes to our attention with disturbing regularity in stark media images. In the faces of famine victims, in the squalor of shanty towns, in the destruction of Earth's natural resources, in the desperate struggle with impoverished soils, we see the differences between the real world and the ideal. Some would say that this is an inevitable fact of life for those affected by it.

Raw figures for population do not, of course, tell us the whole story. There are other aspects which need consideration. World population growth curves show an average growth rate. Like all averages it is calculated from a range of data, in this case data from different parts of the world. Figure 3.9 shows the variation in rates of population increase in different countries.

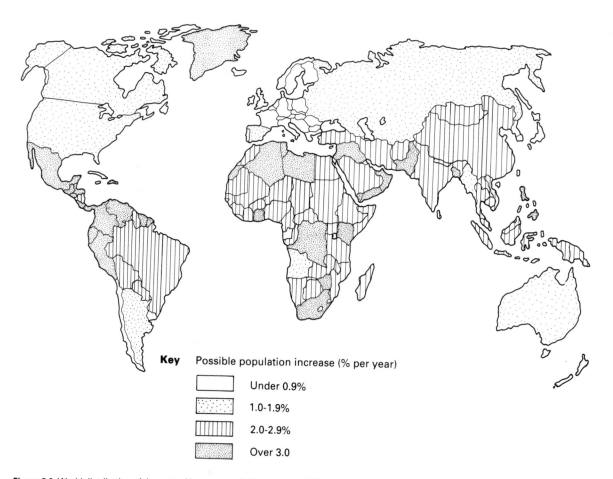

Key Possible population increase (% per year)

	Under 0.9%
	1.0-1.9%
	2.0-2.9%
	Over 3.0

Figure 3.9 World distribution of the natural human population increase, 1980

18. What makes the difference between the real world and the ideal world?

19. Look at the lower limit for population increase shown in Fig.3.9 for the USA (1.0-1.9% per year) and for Mexico (over 3% per year). Using these figures, roughly how long will it take for each of those countries to double their respective populations?

You will remember that present estimates put the doubling time for world population at about 40 years. It is all too easy, therefore, to look at Fig.3.9 and to lay the blame for the current threat of overpopulation on those countries like Mexico with the highest rates of population increase. This conclusion could also be drawn by considering simultaneously the data in Fig.3.10.

At first sight rapid population increase in countries least able to support large populations make little sense. Indeed there are some people who think that such countries are responsible for their own difficulties. Such views would be more acceptable if they were consistent. Far too often, however, their world is a single world in respect of the exploitation of its resources but a divided world in respect of the use and distribution of its produce. A closer consideration of such countries will identify a mixture of social, cultural, economic, religious, educational, developmental and historical reasons for their population explosions. We will return to this later.

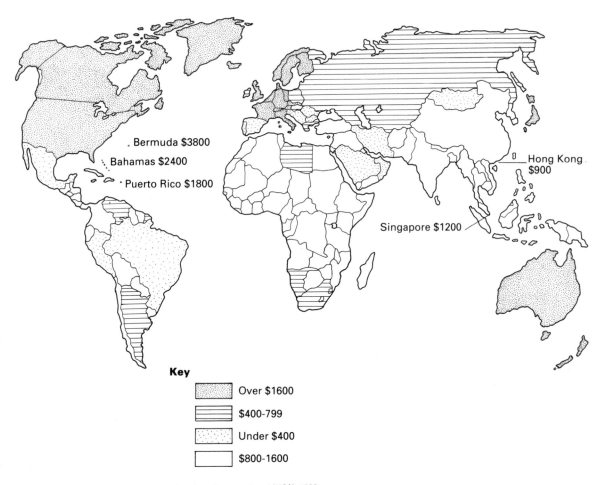

Figure 3.10 World figures of gross national product per head (US$), 1980

The **demographic transition model** or **theory** attempts to relate rates of **population increase** with cultural development. This model is outlined in Fig.3.11. Remember that it is a 'model' and further, that it has been derived largely from European experience and may not translate to other parts of the world.

If the model holds true for other countries then different parts of the world can be observed at different stages. This model adds another layer of complexity to the interpretation of raw population statistics but it does allow for the interpretation of certain otherwise anomalous situations.

Q 20. How can you use the transition model to explain the similarity in population increase between Uruguay and West Germany (both under 0.9%)?

21. Use Figs.3.9 and 3.11 to identify countries or parts of the world which might be in stage two and stage three of the demographic model?

22. Try to characterise the kind of societies which approximate to the four stages of the demographic model.

One of the consequences of such recent variations in patterns of population increase is likely to be variations in population structure. This is the second aspect of human population growth which demands our attention.

Population pyramids are a representation of the structure of a population with respect to age and sex. Figure 3.12 shows the change in population structure in the UK over the 90 years from 1891 to 1980.

Q 23. What, in your opinion, is the single most significant difference in the population structures of 1891 and 1980? How can this difference be explained?

24. In which age group is the single most significant difference in *sex ratios* (the proportion of males to females) throughout the period 1891 - 1980? What explanation can you offer for this? Would you expect the trend to continue into the future?

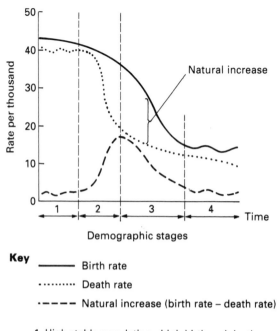

Key

——— Birth rate

·········· Death rate

·—·—·— Natural increase (birth rate – death rate)

1 High stable population - high birth and death rates
2 Expanding stage - birth rate remains high but death rate (mortality) decreases
3 Late expanding stage - population continues to increase but at a lower rate because birth rate declines
4 Low stable population - low birth rate and low mortality

Figure 3.11 A demographic transition model for populations of European countries demonstrating the stages in the population cycle. This is a general principle based on European countries and assumes that all populations grow in a similar way.

demography the study of statistics of population numbers, births, deaths, etc, as illustrating the conditions of life in communities

transition theory populations change from a high death rate/ high birth rate situation through a high birth rate /moderate death rate, to a low birth rate/ low death rate situation, as a society becomes industrialised. The death rate decreases before the birth rate decreases, so there is a large population in the transition period (demographic transition)

annual population increase the number or percentage of extra people each year due to a natural rate of increase and migration. The difference between birth rate and death rate is called natural rate of increase

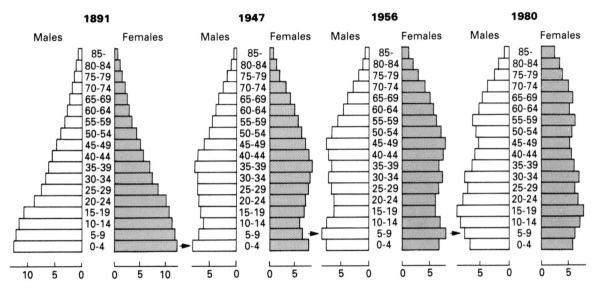

Figure 3.12 Population pyramids for the UK since 1891. The length of each horizontal bar represents the percentage of the total population in a particular age group at the time of the census

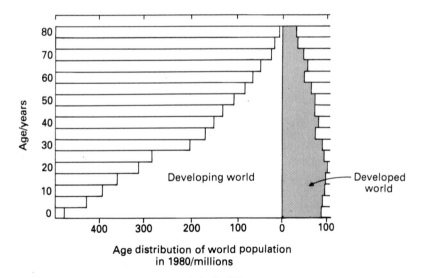

Figure 3.13 Age distribution of world population in 1980

Population pyramids offer us an interesting view of the past. They allow us to identify, for example, the decline in birth rate of the depression years between the World Wars, the post Second World War bulge in the birth rate and the 1960s bulge and to speculate about their causes. More important, however, is their use in predicting population structure in the future and planning to meet the demands that it will make. In this respect, a glance at Fig.3.13 will be enough to show the difference in demands which will be made on the developed and the developing worlds in the future.

Whilst the developed countries have to prepare for an increasing proportion of elderly people in their populations, the developing nations have almost 50 per cent of their populations under the age of 20. Wise governments will look ahead and plan investment according to the predictable demands. For the elderly, this means appropriate medical and welfare provision and the provision of resources and opportunities for a more active and constructive retirement than in the past.

For the young, it means a totally different medical provision, education and preparation for work but also the provision of suitable employment opportunities. These demands are immediate.

In the long term the need is for a rolling programme which in the developed world recognises a declining proportion of reproductive individuals and in the developing world recognises the opposite.

In the real world there is one inevitable consequence of these trends and that is the need for population control. This may seem an obvious conclusion and one to which many people see an equally obvious corollary, i.e. the need for birth control. Obvious because the alternative means of regulating population (abortion, infanticide and euthanasia), all of which have been used in the past, are ethically unacceptable to our society.

Abortion (the premature termination of a pregnancy) and euthanasia (the premature termination of the life of a person at his or her own request) have their supporters in particular circumstances, but to most people their use as a means of regulating population are, like the use of infanticide, repugnant.

What is 'obvious' to one person can, however, be wholly unacceptable to others. In a complex world with many different cultures, religious beliefs, social structures, economic conditions and educational opportunities, the introduction of a birth control programme is equally complex. This perhaps helps to explain why *Unicef*, *Unesco*, *WHO* and *OECD* have, so far, had little success in encouraging poor countries to adopt such programmes. In order to understand the situation

---

Unicef United Nations (International) Children's (Emergency) Fund

Unesco United Nations Educational, Scientific and Cultural Organisation

WHO World Health Organisation

OECD Organisation for Economic Co-operation and Development

---

we must attempt to empathise with those whose co-operation with birth control programmes is so vital.

Q 25. What do you suppose might be the reactions of people in the following circumstances?

a) A 20 year old Indian woman, married at 15 and now with two children has heard rumours that the loop (IUD) could swim through the blood to the brain, or give the man a shock during sexual intercourse or cause increased menstrual bleeding.

b) A Hindu father of three children, who believes it is a sin to prevent the conception of a child, has been offered a vasectomy.

c) A young educated South American couple, who are devout Catholics, face planning their family using only the rhythm method of contraception (a method with a known failure rate of at least 25%) or repeatedly committing a sin by using the contraceptive pill.

d) A Ugandan peasant farmer, whose wealth can only be measured by the ability of his family to work the land, is offered a free supply of condoms.

e) A 16 year old Sudanese girl, married at 14, one of two surviving children from a family of five is offered contraceptive advice. She has already lost one child of her own, to measles, at the age of 12 weeks.

How do you think people and governments of poorer nations feel about this urgent imposition of birth control by the more affluent developed nations? This is the same problem that has been posed elsewhere in the context of the need for a global approach to pollution and conservation.

Appreciating the complexity of the problem is important but does not solve it.

Even if you do not think that the human population explosion has played a central role (as suggested by Fig.3.8), it remains for whatever reasons a significant contributor to the current human predicament. With the continuing rapid increase in population, we can expect to see environmental resistance expressing itself more forcefully in ways that are already evident.

Malnutrition, if not famine, is a fact of life for many; disease lurks in the wings picking off victims from among the malnourished. 'Living space' in the form of fertile agricultural land will decline by one third between 1990 and 2010 at the present rates of impoverishment.

Thomas Robert Malthus (1766 - 1834) developed the idea that the human population would be wiped out unless its birth rate was limited. Darwin and Wallace were influenced by this idea in their thoughts on the theory of evolution by natural selection. His influence also extended to Marx and Engels, and to the economist, John Maynard Keynes

The question is how will the new set point for the human population be established? Will it be the result of environmental resistance as Malthus predicted, or will human intervention bring about an equilibrium position less brutally? In China the government turned to legislation to limit families to one child. Is this the way forward for all nations?

Answer to question on page 20

Population change = BR – DR + IR – ER.

THE HUMAN LIFE CYCLE

We can think of the human life cycle as a sequence of specific stages from conception to death.

■ GROWTH AND DEVELOPMENT

Growth is defined as the permanent increase in size of an individual in the course of its development. This definition allows us to include, as well as increases in size, changes of form (morphological change or development). One illustration of the difference between overall growth and development is provided by Figures 4.1 and 4.2. The growth of different parts of the body at rates different to that of the body as a whole is known as *allometric* growth. An allometric growth curves give us a picture of how development takes place.

Q 1. How can the different growth patterns seen in in Figs.4.1 and 4.2 be explained?

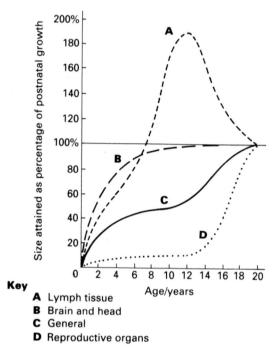

Key
A Lymph tissue
B Brain and head
C General
D Reproductive organs

Figure 4.2 Growth curves of different parts of the human body expressed as a percentage of total growth achieved between birth and 20 years of age

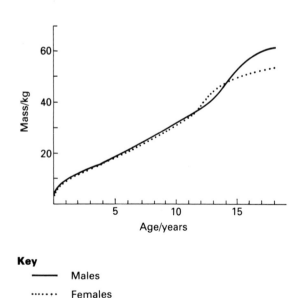

Key

⎯⎯⎯ Males

······· Females

Figure 4.1 Growth curves of human body mass for boys and girls up to the age of 18

This boy has the inherited genetic defect which compresses the life cycle - Cockayne's disease. Cells isolated from the body and grown in culture have a short life. Research into the metabolism of these cells could help us to understand how the human body ages

We can distinguish between internal factors and external (environmental) factors that influence growth, although the growth rate is regulated by interactions between internal and environmental influences.

Growth involves three distinct processes:
• cell division.
• assimilation of materials.
• cell expansion.

The major external factor influencing human growth is thus the supply of materials, i.e. the diet. The rapid rate of growth in the first postnatal year may reflect the rapid cell expansion of the cells produced in the embryo. This is possible due to an increased intake of materials after birth. Throughout the 20 or so years of human growth protein should make up at least 20 per cent of the diet to provide the building materials of newly formed cells. The tragic results of protein deficiency in the human diet are seen in the familiar photographs of the victims of *kwashiorkor* - the pot-bellied children ironically bloated by protein starvation.

A victim of kwashiorkor in Somalia. Tragically a picture far too familiar to us in the latter half of the twentieth century. The hugely distended abdomen is due to gas released by bacteria in the small intestine and stomach

Q 2. Growth is complete by early adulthood. Why do adults still require their diets to contain 15 per cent protein?

Other components of the diet contribute directly or indirectly to growth in ways that are too varied to be included here. One example, however, can be singled out to illustrate the interaction between diet and hormones. This interaction is one of the important internal factors affecting growth. Iodine is an important constituent of *thyroxin*, the hormone which regulates metabolic rate. Iodine deficiency results in stunted physical growth and mental development. Several other hormones influence human growth and development, notably *pituitary growth hormone* (the lack of which produces dwarfism), and *testosterone* and *oestrogen* (which are responsible for the development of secondary sexual characteristics in boys and girls respectively).

The other important internal factor affecting growth is genetic constitution. Everyone knows that physical stature and build are inherited within families. The principle of the interaction between factors is reinforced by the fact that the genetic influence on growth is mediated by hormones. There is also evidence that at least some hormones exert their action on cells by operating as switching mechanisms at the level of DNA, i.e. by switching particular genes on or off.

Growth as a permanent increase in size is effectively complete in humans by early adulthood. However, this development has not only physical but also sexual, mental and emotional aspects which are, to some extent, independent of increase in size. Human development through the life cycle differs from that of other mammals. Three features are particularly different.

• Human babies have big heads in proportion to their body size (this is related to a human's highly developed brain). The relative helplessness of the human baby at birth compared to other primates is probably due to the need for birth to take place before the head becomes too large to pass through the birth canal. In other words, this vulnerability is the price we pay for our highly developed brains.

• Compared with our closest non-human relatives we experience a long childhood. For many years we are dependent on parental care. We achieve sexual maturity at a later age than other animals. Even at physical sexual maturity, several further years elapse before emotional and social maturity in human society. Explanations have been offered for this too, in terms of the complexity of learning that is involved in human development.

• For our size we have an unexpectedly long life span (Fig 4.3). Life expectancy in Britain has risen to an average close to 70 years over the last century (Fig 4.4). It is therefore tempting to explain this in terms of improved nutrition and medicine. The biblical reference to 'three score years and ten' as the human span could suggest that our current expectation represents a recovery to that of an earlier period of longevity. There is a danger, however, in extrapolating biblical reference because it would eventually take us back to the golden age of the 900 year old Methuselah!

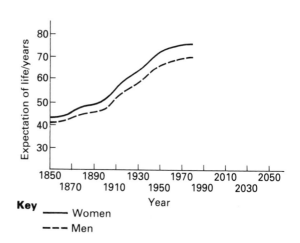

Key
—— Women
--- Men

Figure 4.4 Changes in the life expectancy of men and women since 1850. Two questions are raised by these trends:
(a) Why have women lived longer than men during this period?
(b) Is it possible to predict what human life expectancies will be in 2050?

■ INFANCY, CHILDHOOD AND PARENTAL CARE

Infancy and childhood cover the years between birth and puberty. As we have seen already the rapid prenatal growth continues through the first postnatal year before slowing considerably until puberty. During this time allometric growth results in a change in body proportions (Fig 4.5). Growth of the head and brain is completed at an early age. Development of the immune system reaches a peak of activity as the young child responds to the challenges of disease and the childhood immunisation programme. All other parts of the body follow the overall growth pattern.

Over the same period of growth, parental care changes its pattern with the changing demands of the child. At the outset the mother's role is the more obvious, particularly if she is breast-feeding. The first formed breast milk, called *colostrum*, contains a rich mixture of lactose and protein for nourishment, and antibodies and white blood cells to give short-term defence against disease. Normal human breast milk is more watery than colostrum and is a mixture of lactose, protein, fats and salts. Lactation is stimulated by suckling and breast-feeding can therefore be maintained for several years if necessary. This practice is not

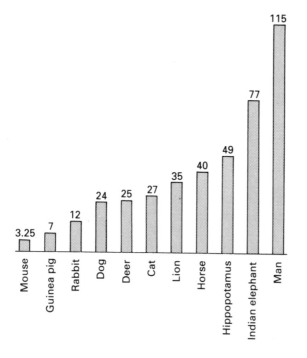

Figure 4.3 Maximum mammalian life spans in years. Most records are for animals in captivity where environmental factors are controlled. In many respects conditions for survival are more favourable than in the wild

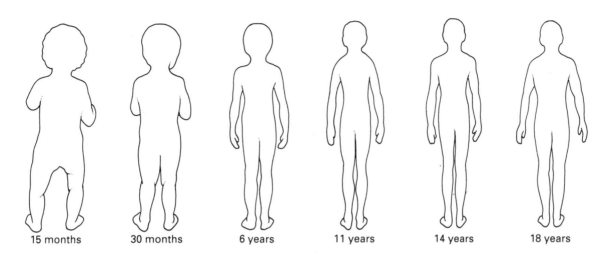

| 15 months | 30 months | 6 years | 11 years | 14 years | 18 years |

Figure 4.5 How the physical proportions of the body change through childhood and adolescence. This illustration shows the same boy at six different ages

unusual in parts of the world where the normal diet for a child could be protein deficient. When a second child is born, the first must be weaned with inevitable risks to its nutrition and health. Hence the name for the condition of protein starvation is kwashiorkor, which can be translated from Ghanaian as 'the rejected one'. In Britain, infants are generally weaned between the sixth and ninth month of postnatal life and transfer gradually to a diet containing more solid foods. The role of a parent as the feeder and protector of the child (as illustrated by breast-feeding) continues in a variety of different ways throughout childhood and beyond.

Q 3. What provisions made by parents could be described as 'protective'?

These and other parental roles can, of course, be successfully carried out in cases where the mother is unable to breast-feed but for mammals like ourselves, it makes biological sense that breast-feeding is the most straightforward way of achieving them.

Q 4. What other parental roles can be identified during the first six months of life?

Beyond those roles which you may have previously identified as broadly protective in

Parents must act as protectors of their children

nature (such as providing clothing, shelter, a physical protective presence and 'censorship', and ensuring appropriate medical care), two other categories will probably be apparent. The parent is also an educator and a socialiser. An understanding of how these two roles are played is perhaps best gained by considering what the human child has to achieve during its development.

Against this background two things become evident:

• Only part of this development takes place during the years of childhood as defined earlier. This reinforces the point that parental care does not stop when the offspring reach puberty. Indeed, at this stage there are parents who would say that parenthood simply becomes more difficult!

• These roles although pre-eminently parental are shared, increasingly as time passes, by other relatives, friends, acquaintances, as well as by institutions like schools and clubs.

The whole pattern of development can be seen as progress towards independence, but independence within a social framework and existence. It involves *maturation*, i.e. the development and realisation of the individual's inherited traits, and *learning* which is the acquisition of knowledge and skills based on experience. We shall return to this idea later.

Child development is the subject of many detailed books which you could consult for more information if you are interested. The following account is selected to illustrate the skills which are acquired in achieving independence and socialisation and which are recognisable from most people's experience.

From the moment of birth an infant shows a remarkable capacity to adapt to a new and comparatively hostile environment. Within a very short time its lungs take over the role of supplying oxygen and its digestive system the role of supplying food. Its metabolism begins to generate heat to maintain body temperature. Its circulatory system closes off two circulatory channels (the foramen ovale between right and left atria and the ductus arteriosus between aorta and pulmonary artery) and substitutes adult haemoglobin for fetal haemoglobin.

Q 5. Figure 4.6 shows the position of the foramen ovale and the ductus arteriosus in the fetal circulation. Their purpose is to allow blood to bypass the fetal lungs. What would be the consequence in postnatal life if these were not closed off at birth?

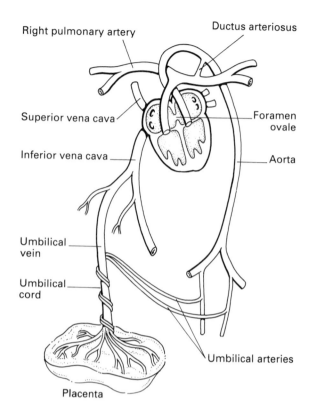

Figure 4.6 Human fetal circulation

At birth the **autonomic nervous system** is relatively underdeveloped and cannot precisely regulate and stabilise breathing rate, heart rate, feeding rhythm and sleeping rhythm. Within a few months **homeostasis** becomes established.

All of these changes represent physiological progress towards independence but this trend is more obvious in the development of muscle control and co-ordination. A newborn child has most of the important reflexes operational. However, he or she shows a good deal of aimless unco-ordinated movement and relatively limited sensory development in those areas important in

---

autonomic nervous system in vertebrates, a system of motor nerve fibres supplying the smooth muscles and glands of the body (see *Biology Advanced Studies - Human Systems*)

homeostasis the maintenance of the internal environment (inside the organism) within narrow controlled limits

movement. By about 15 months the baby can, unsteadily but without help, be walking. Throughout the development of these skills maturation and learning can be seen working together. (Note: The physiological processes are explained in more detail in *Biology Advanced Studies - Human Systems*.)

A further step towards independence and, at the same time, the first step towards socialisation comes with the beginning of *communication*. Communication provides the means of self-expression and of active participation in the world outside and is one of the main aspects of being human. It starts with gestures, in particular facial gestures such as smiles. Pre-speech forms of communication also include 'crying' and 'babbling'. Babbling is considered to be the more important as it leads directly into speech. Just as certain reflexes seem to be innate there is evidence to suggest that certain aspects of speech and language are a part of human genetic inheritance. Once again, however, learning plays a major part in the development of speech (Fig.4.7). With the learning of vocabulary comes a clear demonstration of the skill of *understanding*. At first comprehension comes from association between the word and the object or gesture. With time, objects and gestures become less important.

Communication and play are important for *knowledge* to be built up. In babyhood most play is solitary rather than social but as time passes play becomes a natural vehicle for socialisation.

Constant reference has been made throughout this account to the dual role of maturation and learning in development. This has been deliberate because it throws into focus the so-called 'nature versus nurture' debate which underlies the history of the theories of child development. Each side in this debate has its origin in the fairly distant past. On the 'nature' side is the idea of predestination. On the 'nurture' side is the idea of the *tabula rasa*, or blank sheet, on which the individual's destiny can be written and shaped by the social environment.

In modern terms they can be described as the hereditary philosophy based on genes and innate instincts, and the environmentalist philosophy based on the possibility of changing human nature by upbringing.

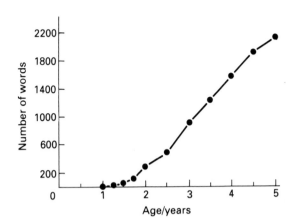

Figure 4.7 The rapid increase of vocabulary during early childhood. Most young children today speak more fluently than children in the past. Can you suggest possible reasons for this improvement

Modern developmental psychologists favour an interaction between heredity and environment (i.e. between maturation and learning) as the previous account suggests. Two of the most influential of these psychologists are Jean Piaget and Erik Erikson. Each has proposed a stage by stage development to maturity through which an individual will pass during childhood and adolescence. Piaget's scheme emphasises the growth of intelligence as a means of adapting to the environment. Erikson pays more attention to the growth of personality by the overcoming of a sequential series of fundamental problems. He considers that the emotional aspects of life play a critical role in this process. Each proposes a rough timetable and in some ways their schemes can be considered to be complementary. A brief outline of each theory appears in Table 4.1.

An interesting recent observation on the 'nature versus nurture' debate has been made by Richard Dawkins in his book *The Selfish Gene*. The central thesis of the book is that evolution does not work at the level of survival of the individual of the species but at the level of the gene. The gene, he says, is 'selfish' and uses us - mere survival machines - in ways that are often far from *humanitarian*. Thus the development of an individual concerned for the common good and more especially for the

and a boy *could* become able to father a child. Fifty per cent of girls reach this point between the ages of 12 and 14 years; fifty per cent of boys between the ages of 13.5 and 15.5 years. The variability of sexual maturity is clear from the 50 per cent of individuals who reach it before or after these ages. The release of testosterone from the testes and oestrogen from the ovaries at this time is responsible for the development of secondary sexual characteristics - that is, those that have no direct involvement in reproduction.

The list of these characteristics in Table 4.2 will be familiar but their lack of direct involvement in reproduction may be open to personal interpretation of the word 'reproduction'.

Q 7. What is the definition of 'reproduction'? Does this include or exclude the involvement of all secondary sexual characteristics?

8. What indirect purposes are served by these characteristics?

Boys	Girls
Hair Pubic hair appears about one year after the testes and penis have started to increase in size. Axillary and facial hair appear when the pubic hair has already completed its growth, as does body hair	*Hair* Pubic hair appears after hip and breast development is well under way. Axillary hair begins to appear after the menarche, as does facial hair. Body hair appears on the limbs late in puberty
Skin The skin becomes coarser, less transparent, and sallow in color, and the pores enlarge	*Skin* The skin becomes coarser, thicker, and slightly sallow, and the pores enlarge
Glands The sebaceous, or oil-producing, glands in the skin enlarge and become more active, which may cause acne. The apocrine glands in the armpits start to function, and perspiration increases as puberty progresses	*Glands* The sebaceous and apocrine glands become more active as puberty progresses. Clogging of the sebaceous glands can cause acne, while the apocrine glands in the armpits produce perspiration, which is especially heavy and pungent just before and during the menstrual cycle
Muscles The muscles increase markedly in size and strength, thus giving shape to the arms, legs, and shoulders	*Muscles* The muscles increase in size and strength, especially in the middle of puberty and towards the end, thus giving shape to the shoulders, arms, and legs
Voice Voice changes begin after some pubic hair has appeared. The voice first becomes husky and later drops in pitch, increases in volume, and acquires a pleasanter tone. Voice breaks are common when maturing is rapid	*Voice* The voice becomes fuller and more melodious. Huskiness and breaks in the voice are rare among girls.
	Hips The hips become wider and rounder as a result of the enlargement of the pelvic bone and the development of subcutaneous fat
	Breasts Shortly after the hips start to enlarge, the breasts begin to develop. The nipples enlarge and protrude, and as the mammary glands develop, the breasts become larger and rounder.

Table 4.2 Changes occurring at puberty - secondary sexual characteristics

Because of the nature of the changes that take place (both physically, mentally and emotionally) between childhood and adolescence it is not surprising that this forms a significant stage in Erikson's theory of development. For Erikson the problem to be solved is that of 'identity'. The need to answer the question, 'who am I?, physically, emotionally, sexually and socially, also demonstrates the importance of Piaget's parallel developmental stage of abstract thought (see Table 4.1).

Today we accept that puberty is an event of early teenage years. At the turn of the nineteenth century, however, girls did not reach puberty until 17 or 18. The more widely accepted explanations for this change are the improvements in nutrition and the reduction in childhood diseases that have been made over the last century. A further suggestion which, although more speculative, you may like to discuss, is the effect in the latter part of this century of the powerful images in film, television and advertising of the desirability of the achievement of particular secondary characteristics. Such strong emotional influences, it is argued, may have an effect on the pituitary gland and bring about the earlier onset of puberty through wish fulfilment.

■ MATURITY AND PARENTHOOD

The middle years of the human life cycle see relatively little biological change in the body, but it is the time when reproduction (and the start of new life cycles) occurs.

Maturity and parenthood, however, do not always occur together. Today, as well as the anatomical and physiological aspects of reproduction, we need to consider the social and ethical questions. You could begin to have some of these questions in mind while reading this and the following chapters. You may have opinions on such questions now when you discuss them with your colleagues. Consider and discuss them again at the end of the book.

Q 9. What is the precise meaning of the word conception?

10. What is the meaning of contraception and how is it different from abortion?

11. To what extent has the contraceptive pill promoted greater opportunities for sexual equality in society?

12. If a woman agrees to carry a fertilised egg for another woman whose own uterus rejects implantation, whose baby is it when it is born?

In evolutionary terms, human reproduction can be viewed as very efficient. This present-day efficiency has resulted from the combined effects of our mammalian biology and our uniquely human technology. Technology, including ultrasonic scanning, amniocentesis, incubators and other forms of pre- and post-natal care, is considered by some to be artificial. However, as a product of human intelligence, it is as much a part of the evolutionary process as, for example, the capacity of a chimpanzee to use objects as tools in its natural habitat. Whether the *application* of such human knowledge is 'un-natural' is a question for debate.

The purely biological factors of structure and function represent stages in the evolution of reproduction in the animal kingdom. Sexual, as opposed to asexual reproduction, internal fertilisation, more or less continuous and non-seasonal female receptiveness, placental pregnancy, relatively prolonged pregnancy, and eventually, enhanced and protracted parental care are all features contributing to the efficiency of human reproduction.

13. What contribution has each of these six factors made to human reproductive efficiency? What features of human reproduction show it to be efficient?

It is these factors which we shall examine first.

■ HUMAN REPRODUCTIVE SYSTEMS

(For further details on the reproductive systems *see Biology Advanced Studies - Human Systems*)

The event which defines sexual reproduction is fertilisation - the fusion of a single male gamete (sperm) with a single female gamete (ovum). The structure of the male and female reproductive systems (Figs.4.9 and 4.10) is suited to produce the gametes (gametogenesis), to bring them together and, in the case of the female system, to nurture the fertilised ovum, embryo and fetus and

eventually to give birth to a baby. You will have a clearer understanding of the structures if the functions are borne in mind and vice versa.

Although it is clear from Figs.4.9 and 4.10 that at sexual maturity there are substantial differences between the sexes, this not true at all stages of human development. Studies of human embryos show that the gonads in both sexes begin development inside the body and are not distinguishable at first. The descent of the testes and the subsequent growth of the male organs in a 'male' fetus are controlled by the levels of testosterone produced by the mother.

If this hormonal stimulus is absent a genetically male fetus will fail to develop external male genital organs and may not do so until puberty when testosterone is produced in his own body. Such apparent spontaneous sex changes are documented in medical records.

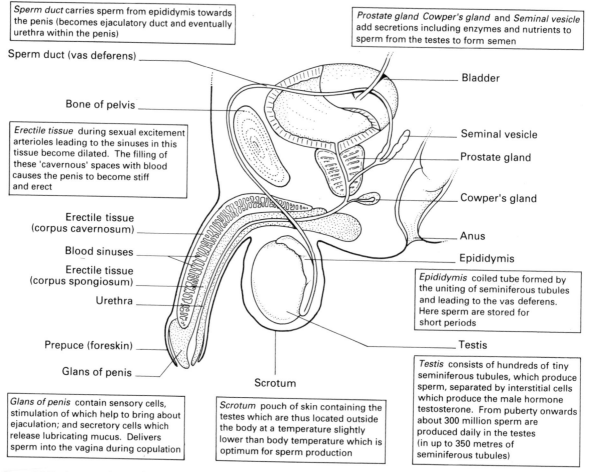

Sperm duct carries sperm from epididymis towards the penis (becomes ejaculatory duct and eventually urethra within the penis)

Prostate gland Cowper's gland and *Seminal vesicle* add secretions including enzymes and nutrients to sperm from the testes to form semen

Sperm duct (vas deferens)

Bone of pelvis

Erectile tissue during sexual excitement arterioles leading to the sinuses in this tissue become dilated. The filling of these 'cavernous' spaces with blood causes the penis to become stiff and erect

Erectile tissue (corpus cavernosum)

Blood sinuses

Erectile tissue (corpus spongiosum)

Urethra

Prepuce (foreskin)

Glans of penis

Glans of penis contain sensory cells, stimulation of which help to bring about ejaculation; and secretory cells which release lubricating mucus. Delivers sperm into the vagina during copulation

Scrotum

Scrotum pouch of skin containing the testes which are thus located outside the body at a temperature slightly lower than body temperature which is optimum for sperm production

Bladder

Seminal vesicle

Prostate gland

Cowper's gland

Anus

Epididymis

Epididymis coiled tube formed by the uniting of seminiferous tubules and leading to the vas deferens. Here sperm are stored for short periods

Testis

Testis consists of hundreds of tiny seminiferous tubules, which produce sperm, separated by interstitial cells which produce the male hormone testosterone. From puberty onwards about 300 million sperm are produced daily in the testes (in up to 350 metres of seminiferous tubules)

Figure 4.9 The human male reproductive system

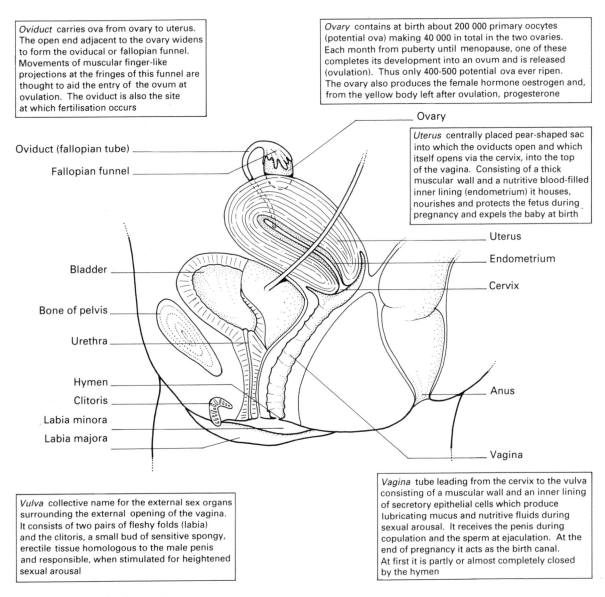

Oviduct carries ova from ovary to uterus. The open end adjacent to the ovary widens to form the oviducal or fallopian funnel. Movements of muscular finger-like projections at the fringes of this funnel are thought to aid the entry of the ovum at ovulation. The oviduct is also the site at which fertilisation occurs

Ovary contains at birth about 200 000 primary oocytes (potential ova) making 40 000 in total in the two ovaries. Each month from puberty until menopause, one of these completes its development into an ovum and is released (ovulation). Thus only 400-500 potential ova ever ripen. The ovary also produces the female hormone oestrogen and, from the yellow body left after ovulation, progesterone

Ovary

Uterus centrally placed pear-shaped sac into which the oviducts open and which itself opens via the cervix, into the top of the vagina. Consisting of a thick muscular wall and a nutritive blood-filled inner lining (endometrium) it houses, nourishes and protects the fetus during pregnancy and expels the baby at birth

Oviduct (fallopian tube)

Fallopian funnel

Uterus

Endometrium

Cervix

Bladder

Bone of pelvis

Urethra

Hymen

Clitoris

Labia minora

Labia majora

Anus

Vagina

Vulva collective name for the external sex organs surrounding the external opening of the vagina. It consists of two pairs of fleshy folds (labia) and the clitoris, a small bud of sensitive spongy, erectile tissue homologous to the male penis and responsible, when stimulated for heightened sexual arousal

Vagina tube leading from the cervix to the vulva consisting of a muscular wall and an inner lining of secretory epithelial cells which produce lubricating mucus and nutritive fluids during sexual arousal. It receives the penis during copulation and the sperm at ejaculation. At the end of pregnancy it acts as the birth canal. At first it is partly or almost completely closed by the hymen

Figure 4.10 The human female reproductive system

■ Gametogenesis

Sexual maturity in girls and boys occurs at the onset of the formation of ova (oogenesis) and spermatozoa (spermatogenesis). This is shown as a schematic diagram in Fig.4.11. Note that in the process of meiosis the chromosome number is reduced from 46 to 23 (shown in the diagram as 2*n* and *n*). Transverse section drawings (Fig.4.12) through an ovary and seminiferous tubule, where these processes take place, demonstrate that this

sequence also has a spatial organisation. This is seen most clearly in the seminiferous tubules. Spermatogonia cells form the germinal cell layer at the perimeter of the tubule. They multiply, grow and mature and migrate inwards towards the lumen (the space through the centre of the tube). Through this lumen the mature sperm eventually travel to the epididymis. Sertoli cells appear to nourish and control cells throughout spermatogenesis.

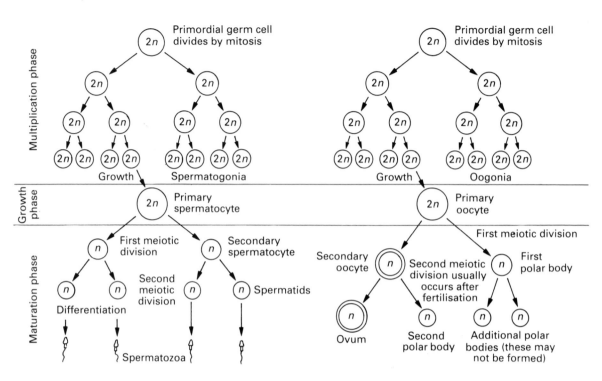

Figure 4.11 Gametogenesis: a schematic diagram to show the process of (a) spermatogenesis in a mammalian testis and (b) oogenesis in a mammalian ovary

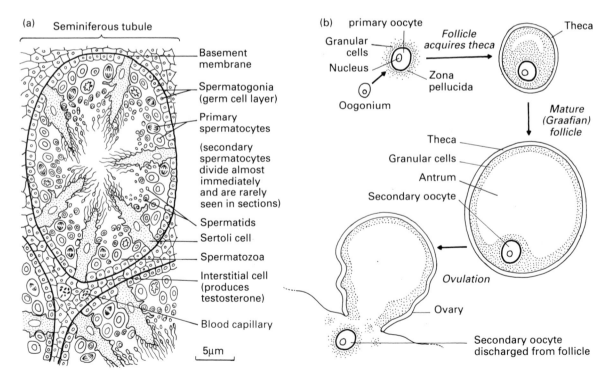

Figure 4.12 Gametogenesis: (a) TS seminiferous tubule, (b) TS ovary

In the ovary the pattern is complicated by four factors and, therefore, although the organisation is still there it is by no means so obvious.

• The primordial germ cells once again form an outer germ layer of the ovary but the multiplication and growth phases of oogenesis take place during fetal development. A baby girl is born with primary oocytes in her ovaries. They remain at this stage until puberty.

• Maturing primary oocytes move in towards the centre but they do so within a follicle consisting of a cluster of granular secretory cells (performing the same function as Sertoli cells in the testis) and, later, a limiting membrane called the *theca*.

• The maturation phase begins with the first meiotic division. In the process of ovulation the 'egg' which leaves the ovary is really a secondary oocyte.

• The interim product of oogenesis is discharged from the ovary not through a central lumen, but via a return of the mature (Graafian) follicle to the outer lining of the ovary where it forms a swelling and finally ruptures.

One further distinction between oogenesis and spermatogenesis involves their relative productivity. A woman produces a single ovum at approximately monthly intervals between menarche (puberty) and the menopause. A man produces approximately 300 million sperm daily, from puberty until extreme old age.

Q 14 Why should there be so many sperm compared to the number of 'eggs' produced?

The woman's monthly ,menstrual, cycle (Fig.4.13) has a regulatory influence on human reproductive potential. It restricts the usual number of offspring

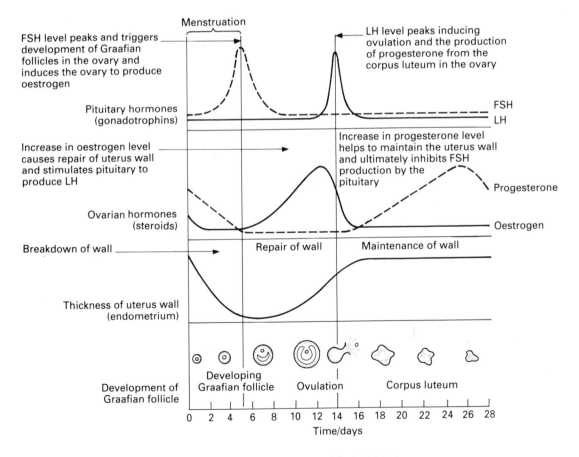

Figure 4.13 The human menstrual cycle. FSH = follicle stimulating hormone. LH = luteinising hormone

per pregnancy to one. As a result of the long period of pregnancy and postnatal breast-feeding, it also regulates her potential fertility. In spite of this the potential is still high as we can see from human population growth figures (see page 23). Human social history is strongly and increasingly influenced by human fertility, environmental resistance and our technological responses to human population expansion.

■ Copulation

Sexual arousal in response to a variety of erotic stimuli is accompanied by a number of physiological changes. These include an increase in breathing rate, heart rate, blood pressure and blood supply to the genital regions. The latter causes the woman's labia and clitoris to swell and increase in sensitivity and her vaginal lining to secrete mucus. In the man, the erectile tissues of the penis swell causing it to become erect and mucus is secreted by the glands at its tip. This fluid helps to neutralise the acid conditions in the vagina which can inhibit or even kill sperm. It also lubricates the thrusting movement of the penis in

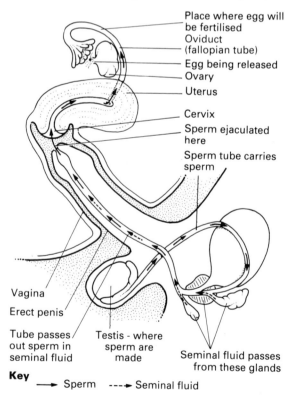

Place where egg will be fertilised
Oviduct (fallopian tube)
Egg being released
Ovary
Uterus
Cervix
Sperm ejaculated here
Sperm tube carries sperm
Vagina
Erect penis
Tube passes out sperm in seminal fluid
Testis - where sperm are made
Seminal fluid passes from these glands

Key  Sperm ----► Seminal fluid

Figure 4.14 Human copulation

the vagina during copulation (see Fig.4.14). The continued stimulation of the sensitive touch receptors in the tip of the penis causes the emptying of a mixture of sperm and seminal fluid into his urethra and its expulsion as semen from the penis at ejaculation. This coincides with male orgasm (the physiological and emotional climax of sexual intercourse associated with extreme pleasure). The female orgasm can result from the rhythmic movement of the penis against the clitoris, labia and vaginal wall and it involves the contraction of an equivalent set of muscles in the vagina and uterus. It may aid the entry of sperm into the uterus but is not essential for fertilisation.

Q 15. There is an association between orgasm and the pleasure centres of the brain. Do you think it is valid to interpret orgasm as an incentive towards: a) reproduction, b) pair bonding?

■ Fertilisation

The sperm have to journey from the cervix, where they are delivered at ejaculation, to the top of the oviduct, where fertilisation occurs. The difficulty of the journey is best reflected in the fact that of the 300 million sperm released in a single ejaculation only a few hundred reach the ovum.

Q 16. Can you suggest any explanation for this apparently huge wastage of effort and potential?

The presence of hormones (prostaglandins) causes contractions of the uterus and oviduct. It is these contractions which are thought to be largely responsible for the passive movement of the sperm. The active swimming of the sperm may be of significance only in the final penetration of the ovum.

Semen contains sugars as fuel and has a pH of 7.3 to neutralise the potentially spermicidal acidity in the vagina. There is no evidence of a chemical attraction between the sperm and the ovum although it seems strange that such an organised sequence of events should culminate in a random collision of two gametes.

The process of mammalian fertilisation itself is far from random, involving a well-defined sequence of events which are summarised in Fig.4.15. The sequence of interactions between sperm and the female reproductive system has been extensively studied in mice.

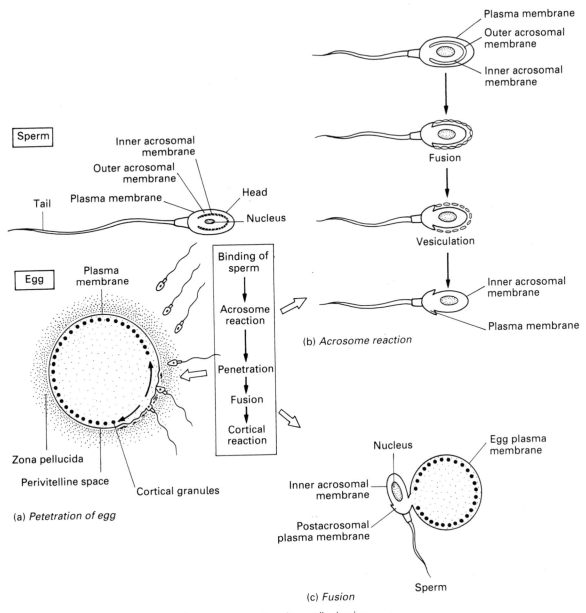

Figure 4.15 (a) The structure of a mammalian sperm and egg based on studies in mice, (b) events leading up to fertilisation based on the same studies of mice

From these studies on mice the following account has been compiled:

• *Capacitation*: ejaculated sperm have to undergo a process involving changes on the sperm's surface as a necessary preliminary step to the acrosome reaction. This takes place in the female reproductive tract.

• *Binding of sperm*: ovulated eggs, arrested at metaphase II of meiosis, are surrounded by a mass of cells. Sperm must first make their way through these cells before binding to specific receptor sites on the *zona pellucida* (the thick transparent membrane surrounding the fully formed ovum in a Graafian follicle).

• *Acrosome reaction and penetration*: the acrosome is, in effect, a sac of enzymes the most significant of which, acrosin, is a protease capable of dissolving a passage through the zona pellucida. Fusion at many points between the plasma membrane of the sperm and the outer acrosomal membrane releases the enzymes allowing the sperm to penetrate as far as the perivitelline space of the egg.

• *Fusion and cortical reaction*: the remaining plasma membrane of the sperm fuses with the plasma membrane of the egg and the sperm head is drawn into the egg. The cortical reaction, in which cortical granules fuse with the plasma membrane and initiate a hardening of the zona pellucida, is thought to be responsible for preventing *polyspermy* (i.e. fertilisation by more than one sperm). However, a more rapid response has been detected in sea urchin eggs involving a significant change in the electrical potential difference across the egg membrane within a few seconds of fertilisation. Echinoderms, like the sea urchin, provided the first insight into sperm-egg fusion over 100 years ago. What we now know of mammalian fertilisation follows the echinoderm pattern. This rapid response barrier to polyspermy may well operate in mammals too.

The final events of fertilisation are the completion of the second meiotic division of the egg, followed by the duplication of the chromatids from both sperm and egg in preparation for mitosis. It is not, however, until two or three mitotic divisions of the zygote have occurred that the new embryonic DNA takes over the direction of the cell's biochemistry. It appears that the enzymes operating in the cytoplasm up to this point are built according to the DNA of the ovum.

The remainder of the account of these events deals specifically with human development.

■ **Early embryonic development and implantation**
Over the next six or seven days, during its journey towards the uterus, the fertilised egg or zygote undergoes a series of mitotic divisions to produce a hollow ball of cells called the blastocyst. It is this stage of development which becomes implanted in the lining (*endometrium*) of the wall of the uterus. Implantation is completed after a further six or seven days. Some ten per cent of fertilised eggs fail to implant. When the blastocyst has implanted, some of its cells (trophoblasts) produce a hormone (chorionic gonadotrophic hormone). This helps to maintain the corpus luteum and so prevent menstruation. This hormone is found in the urine of the mother. Its detection is the basis of the modern pregnancy test.

Q 17. Consider again what is meant by the word conception.

18. At what point in the sequence of events described above does pregnancy begin?

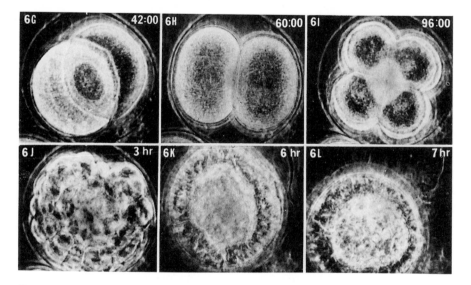

The first stages of growth in a fertilised egg of a rat showing 2-cell, 4-cell and 8-cell stages

These are not just academic questions but ones which may bear significantly on contraception and on the research which has recently culminated in the technique of *in vitro* fertilisation (IVF). Questions such as these that have ethical implications are discussed in Chapter 7. However, it is important to recognise at this point, that the scientist has a necessary and specific role to play in describing, as accurately as current knowledge allows, the biological dimension of such issues to inform those involved in the moral debate.

■ Pregnancy

At the time of implantation the blastocyst has become differentiated into an inner cell mass, which is destined to become the embryo, and a remaining thin outer layer (*chorion*) made up of trophoblast cells. These cells stick to the endometrium of the uterus and quickly divide to form trophoblastic villi. The villi penetrate the endometrium to produce intimate contact between embryonic and maternal tissues. This acts as a primitive placenta (see Fig.4.16).

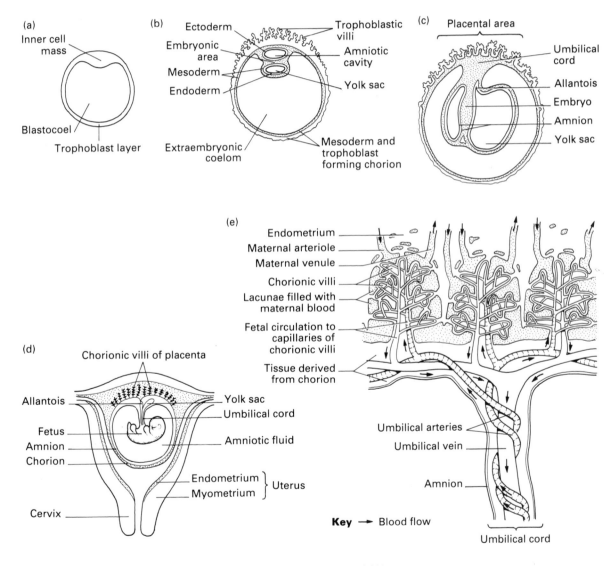

Figure 4.16 The development of fetal membranes and placenta during pregnancy: (a) blastocyst, (b) implantation, (c) developing placenta, (d) developing fetus, (e) details of placenta

The major events are:

(i) The embryonic area (Fig.4.16(b)) differentiates into three layers:

• *ectoderm* (to become skin and nervous system).
• *mesoderm* (to become muscle tissue, skeletal tissues and blood).
• *endoderm* (to become the digestive tract).

(ii) Extensions grow out from the ectoderm to form a fluid-filled cavity completely surrounding the embryo. This is the amniotic cavity, with the amniotic fluid cushioning the embryo against damage caused by physical disturbance.

The yolk sac, formed as an outgrowth of the endoderm, lasts for a very short time.

(iii) Trophoblastic villi are supplemented by chorionic villi as blood vessels grow out of the mesoderm to form the umbilical cord and the placenta (Fig.4.16(c)). The endometrial tissue develops large spaces full of maternal blood which surround the embryonic blood vessels.

By five weeks after implantation the placenta has taken on its full functions. Through the intimate association between maternal and embryonic bloodstreams many materials are transferred between the two circulations. Oxygen, water, mineral salts, glucose, amino acids, vitamins, lipids, hormones and antibodies pass from mother to embryo whilst carbon dioxide, urea and other waste products pass from embryo to mother. The transfer of oxygen is very efficient due to the greater affinity for oxygen of fetal haemoglobin compared with normal haemoglobin.

Later in pregnancy (after about three months), the placenta also produces progesterone. At this time the production of progesterone from the ovary ceases. Later still the placenta secretes oestrogen which eventually plays a role in the preparations for birth, and lactogen which promotes the growth and development of the mammary glands.

 19. The placenta performs the function of five organ systems. What are they?

 20. The maternal and fetal circulations do not join in the placenta. Why is this? Try to think of several reasons.

So far we have been concerned with the environment within the uterus and referred to the developing life within it as the embryo. Table 4.3 which summarises the remarkable development of a human baby from conception to birth, suggests that at 12 weeks the embryo becomes a *fetus*. Fetal age is traditionally reckoned from the start of the last menstrual period and this includes approximately 14 days before fertilisation. The age at birth, of 40 weeks, represents a true fetal age of 38 weeks. This is the *average* age at birth.

Prenatal growth and development is achieved by a highly organised pattern of processes including:

• rapid cell division with relatively little cell expansion.
• cell migration.
• allometric growth morphogenesis.
• cell differentiation morphogenesis.
• storage of fat in later weeks.

In describing this process so 'matter-of-factly' there is a danger that the wonder of it will be lost. Although this is partly a question of individual perception the photograph on the opposite page may help encourage an awareness of the remarkable nature of the nine months of prenatal development.

As the fetus grows, the uterus expands to accommodate it. But during the final few weeks of pregnancy the uterus itself tends to slow the growth of the fetus. This effect will also be exerted by the presence of a second fetus. Twins occur in just over one per cent of successful pregnancies. They may be identical (*monozygotic*) twins resulting from the separation and subsequent development of two cells from a single fertilised egg. They may, on the other hand, be non-identical twins resulting from the fertilisation of two separate eggs by two different sperm.

Weeks	Embryonic fetal length (mm)	Stage of development
2	0.1 (100 μm)	Single cell - zygote
4	2.5	Head end distinct. Limb buds. Heart beating
8	25	Brain developing into main regions. Eyes and ears form. Fingers and toes present. Cartilage skeleton and internal organs begin to form
12	90	(Now called fetus) Digit joints, hair and nails form. Muscles present. Blood made in bone marrow. Kidneys begin to function. Sensitive to touch
16	165	Skin covered with fine hair. Lungs are formed but collapsed. Sweat glands develop
20	240	Lanugo (hair) covers body. Sebaceous glands secrete white, waxy sebum. Lungs, skin and digestive tract well developed. Fetal movements usually detectable by mother
24	300	Skin wrinkles and becomes reddened. Face begins to look human. Nostrils open
28	270	Eyes open. Testes drop in male. Brain enlarges, increasing survival chance if born prematurely
32	425	Bone formation well advanced. Vigorous movements. Kidneys well developed. Fat deposited under skin. Growth slows
36	470	Hair lost from body except head. Turns so that head lies above vagina. At 40 weeks, birth

Table 4.3 Human growth and development before birth

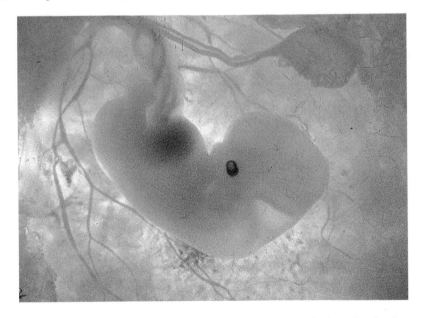

A human embryo at 7 weeks surrounded by the membranes of the chorion (outer layer) and amnion (inner, fluid-filled layer). At this stage of development most of the organ systems and other structures are present. The large dark mass in the body is the liver, which produces red blood cells until the bone marrow takes over this function at about 12 weeks.

■ Birth

Pregnancy is regulated throughout by hormones and so is the process called birth or parturition. What triggers birth is not fully understood but recent evidence suggests that the fetus itself has a role in the timing of its own birth. Like its mother's role, the part it plays is mediated by hormones. The pattern of hormonal changes involved is summarised in Fig.4.17.

Q 21. The fetal adrenal hormone produced to promote its own birth may also cause changes

in the mother. Describe the maternal hormone changes caused:
a) at the placenta?
b) at the pituitary gland?

Towards the end of pregnancy the level of progesterone falls. This reduces its inhibitory effect on uterine contractions and perhaps also on oxytocin production by the pituitary gland. The continued presence of oestrogen is thought to make uterine muscles more sensitive to oxytocin. Oxytocin brings about the onset of a series of

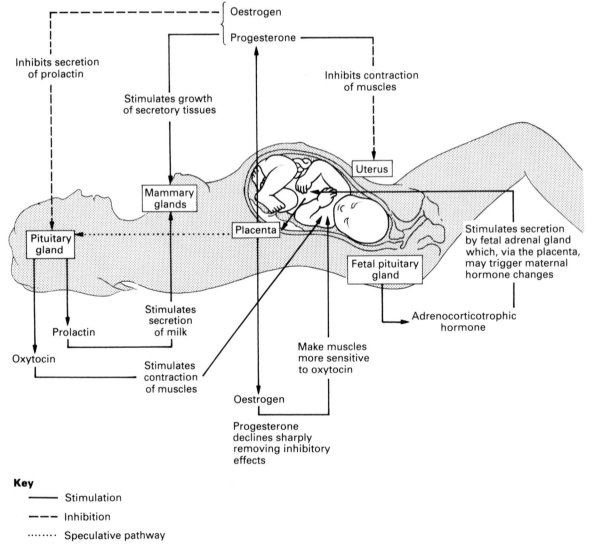

Key

——— Stimulation

– – – Inhibition

········ Speculative pathway

Figure 4.17 Hormonal control of the later stages of pregnancy, birth and lactation. (Notes above the figure refer to hormonal control from the mid-term of pregnancy. Notes below the figure refer to hormonal control at the full-term of pregnancy, i.e. birth)

involuntary uterine contractions which increase in strength and frequency. This sequence leading to birth is called labour. It can be divided into three stages which result from the uterine contractions aided by the mother's voluntary abdominal contractions.

(i) The opening or dilation of the cervix which results in the loss of the cervical plug (the show) and the rupture of the amniotic sac (the breaking of the waters).

(ii) The expulsion of the baby via the cervix and vagina at which point the umbilical cord is cut.

(iii) The expulsion of the placenta and the remains of the umbilical cord (the afterbirth).

When the placenta has been expelled there is a decline in both progesterone and oestrogen in the mother's circulation. This removes the inhibition of prolactin production, with the result that prolactin is produced and lactation begins. Suckling by the baby stimulates the active expulsion of milk from the nipple of the mammary gland. This is the beginning of postnatal parental care.

Having looked in detail at the sequence of events through an uncomplicated pregnancy to a successful birth, and before considering the rest of the human life cycle, it is an appropriate moment to review some important variations on the theme of human reproduction. In a process as complex as the creation of a new human life, variations which change or disrupt the normal process cannot be unexpected. Discuss which of the following variations you consider to be avoidable but be wary of making moral judgements.

(i) Up to 10 per cent of fertilised eggs fail to implant and of those that implant up to 50 per cent probably do not get past the first two weeks of life in the uterus. They are spontaneously aborted so early that the woman's normal menstruation may only be delayed by a few days, if at all, so that she is usually unaware that an egg has been fertilised. Such an abortion or miscarriage is usually due to the abnormal development of the embryo or its surrounding structures.

Chromosomal abnormalities occur in up to 10 per cent of fertilised eggs but in only 0.5 per cent of new-born babies. This means that as many as

95 per cent of such conceptions are rejected prior to, or immediately after, implantation.

(ii) Genetic factors which do not cause early spontaneous abortion may nevertheless influence the development of the fetus. These may affect nuclear division as in Down's Syndrome and a number of syndromes associated with sex-chromosome abnormalities or decreased numbers of chromosomes.

Alternatively, the effects may be caused by single gene mutations affecting protein synthesis as in cystic fibrosis and haemophilia.
(Further details of these factors are discussed later in Chapter 5 and in *Biology Advanced Studies - Genetics and Evoution*.)

Many genetic abnormalities can now be detected using techniques such as amniocentesis and chorionic villus sampling to obtain fetal cells for examination. Chromosome and protein analysis of these cells can provide evidence of a significant and increasing number of genetic disorders at a stage when parents may wish to consider the termination of the pregnancy.

(iii) The environment in the uterus is created by the mother's condition during pregnancy and this too may influence fetal development.

Clearly the mother's diet will have a direct bearing on the growth of the fetus. She must provide all of the nutrients required for a 'balanced diet' for the fetus but in particular proteins and the minerals iron and calcium. Her own dietary demands also increase in response to a 15 per cent increase in basal metabolic rate, an increase in body mass which could amount to 15 per cent or more and an increase in blood volume. The traditional view of the self-sacrificing mother ensuring that her fetus is well-nourished at her own expense is now being challenged. Recent research associates an increased risk of low birth weight and disease of the newborn with malnourishment of the mother.

The mother's age can also be influential. There are increased risks of Down's Syndrome in pregnancies in women over the age of 35 and of stillbirth and protracted labour in first pregnancies over that age. In the latter case good physical health and fitness can reduce the risks. Increased risks of stillbirth, low birth weight and difficulties in labour are also associated with pregnancies in girls who, at the age of 15 or less, have not completed their own growth.

(iv) As well as regulating the necessary exchange of materials between mother and fetus, the placenta also acts as a protective barrier for the fetus. There are however some harmful factors which can cross the placenta. They are known, collectively as *teratogens*. They include, in particular, certain chemicals and some microbial disease agents as summarised in Table 4.4. Most people now realise that smoking before or during the pregnancy can harm the fetus as well as the mother.

(v) The transfer of antibodies from mother to fetus across the placenta provides passive immunity for a period of six months after birth during which the immune system of the new-born child is developing. This transfer, however, may include rhesus antibodies from a rhesus negative mother to a rhesus positive fetus resulting in the destruction of fetal red blood cells. This can only happen if the mother's blood comes into contact with rhesus positive blood during an earlier pregnancy or birth. Thus second or subsequent rhesus positive babies are most at risk. Women at risk are now identified by blood testing and they can be injected to prevent sensitisation of their own immune system to rhesus positive antigens.

(vi) In circumstances in which a normal birth would represent a significant risk to mother or baby, the baby is delivered by Caesarean section.

Q 22. What circumstances can you suggest in which a Caesarean section might be recommended?

(vii) For a variety of reasons some women are unable to breast-feed their babies. In such cases artificial substitutes are available which are constituted to match, as closely as possible, the properties of breast milk. There are, however, significant limitations within which they operate. Whilst nutritionally a good match is possible, it is not possible to provide a substitute for the maternal antibodies which are transferred in breast milk and which give passive immunity against a variety of diseases during the vulnerable early months of life.

Q 23. What are the other advantages of breast-feeding?

Teratogen	Effect on development before birth
Carbon monoxide	Reduces oxygen supply to fetal tissues and can result in low birth weight. Some research also suggests it may reduce brain development
Nicotine	Reduces placental blood flow and may cause premature birth and postnatal fits
Alcohol	May reduce birth weight and, if taken in excess, produce fetal alcohol syndrome associated with some degree of mental handicap
Thalidomide Opren	Such prescribed drugs have been implicated in increased risks of deformity
German measles	During first three months of pregnancy may cause deafness, cataract or even brain damage to the fetus
Syphilis	May cause deafness, blindness, mental handicap or even stillbirth
Herpes simplex	May cause meningoencephalitis - a potentially fatal disease of the nervous system (contracted during birth)
AIDS	Information is not yet based on a sufficiently large number of pregnant women who are HIV positive to make definite predictions about the risk. However, it is known that HIV can pass to the unborn child

Table 4.4 The influence of some important chemical and microbial agents (teratogens) that have been shown to interfere with prenatal development

It is no coincidence that in all human cultures sex and death are traditionally taboo subjects. Modern psychology also recognises them as central human preoccupations and has attempted to demystify them. It is against this background that attention should now be turned to the rest of the human life cycle. As suggested elsewhere we need to try to understand the biological dimension of such issues.

■ MENOPAUSE

The middle years of the human life cycle are, for many, taken up with parenthood. During this period and in the absence of serious disease there is relatively little biological change until the onset in women of the menopause. The significance of menopause is implicit in the term 'change-of-life' which is sometimes used to describe it. It is best defined as the time when a woman's reproductive functions cease and is signalled by the cessation of menstrual periods and of the release of eggs from the ovaries. It occurs between the ages of 39 and 50 and because periods may stop suddenly, or gradually become less heavy, or come at greater and greater intervals until they cease completely,

menopause sometimes refers to the whole time, months or even years, during which this happens. The hormonal balance of the body is altered and the change is sometimes accompanied by some physical discomfort and emotional stress but it does not mean a loss of sexual appetite. In contrast to this ending of egg production in women, men continue to produce sperm into their eighties.

Q 24. What explanations can you suggest for this difference between the sexes?

■ AGEING

Throughout these middle years, however, certain changes are taking place which only become evident as they accumulate. They contribute to the process of *senescence* or ageing, a process about which there has been much debate. The question which still remains is whether or not senescence is inevitable. There are some who see the increased human life span recorded in Table 4.5 as the progressive reduction in premature death. As a result of improvements in our environmental conditions, notably nutrition and the control of some infectious disease, people in the West can

	3000 BC (Early Bronze Age)	1150 Bc (Iron Age)	650 BC (Classical Greece)	120 AD (Imperial Rome)	1400 AD (Middle Ages)	1820 AD (Post Napoleonic)	1980 (Today)
Male life expectancy (years)	33.7	38.6	45.0	40.2	37.7	40.2	70.0
Male height (cms)	166.3	166.7	169.8	169.0	169.3	169.8	175.0
Female life expectancy (years)	29.5	31.3	36.2	34.6	31.1	37.3	76.0
Female height (cms)	153.0	154.6	156.3	156.7	157.0	157.6	162.7
No. of births	4.0	3.7	4.3	3.7	4+	3.8	2.2
No. of survivors	1.9	1.5	2.7	2.0	1.6	2.2	2.0
Dental lesions	4.9	6.0	1.0	24.0	10.0	36.0	8.0
World population (millions)	?	?	?	?250	300	900	5000

Table 4.5 Human 'census-type' data tracing fluctuations in growth, longevity and aspects of health over the last 5000 years. You might like to consider: (a) how such data was obtained, (b) how credible it is

now expect to approach closer to the average genetic limit of 85 years for a human life span. The opposing view to the trend shown in Table 4.5 is that the key to considerably greater life expectancy lies in an understanding of the causes of ageing. Research over the past 20 years has shed some light on this.

What then is the current state of our knowledge of the indicators and the causes of ageing? 'Machines wear out and so do people.' Such an analogy between a human and a machine is, however, far too crude.

Q 25. What are the limitations in comparing the wearing out of a machine with the ageing of the human body?

Amongst your answers to this question may be the following:

• the human body is self-repairing.
• the human body is most vulnerable when new.
• the human body increases in strength, up to a certain point, as it gets older.
• the human body has the capacity to learn and to use experience.

It is true that, in time, human tissues begin to deteriorate just like the parts of a machine. A summary of some of the indicators of ageing are shown in Table 4.6. In attempts to find a single unifying cause for ageing, and thereby a means by which it might be countered, researchers have looked for links between these symptoms.

At first the emphasis was placed upon chemical change in low-turnover components like those in connective tissues. The similarity between the stiffening of collagen and the artificial stiffening of animal skin to form leather by tanning led to the

Body tissue/Function	Symptoms of ageing
Body mass	Most men lose up to 10% of body mass between the ages of 65 - 90
Brain mass	Average mass falls by about 10% between the ages of 30 - 90
Rate of nervous conduction	Declines at varying rates up to 15% between the ages of 30 - 90
Cardiac output at rest	Declines by about 30% between the ages of 30 - 90
Renal filtration rate	Declines by 50% between the ages of 30 - 90
Muscle strength	Declines by 50% between ages of 30 - 75
Vital capacity (lungs) and oxygen consumption	Declines by 50% between ages of 30 - 75
Bones	Lose calcium and become more brittle
Soft tissues	Accumulate calcium and cholesterol
Connective tissue:	Increases as a proportion of body mass and becomes hard and inelastic. The effects of this depend on its location and original content of collagen and elastic
• in skeletal tissues (tendon, ligament)	Hardens and contracts causing stooping
• in arteries	Hardens, thickens and loses elasticity
• in skin	Thins, stiffens and shrinks causing wrinkling
Eyes	May lose focusing powers
Ears	Lose cochlear function causing loss of hearing range particularly at high frequency

Table 4.5 Indicators of the process of ageing of the human body

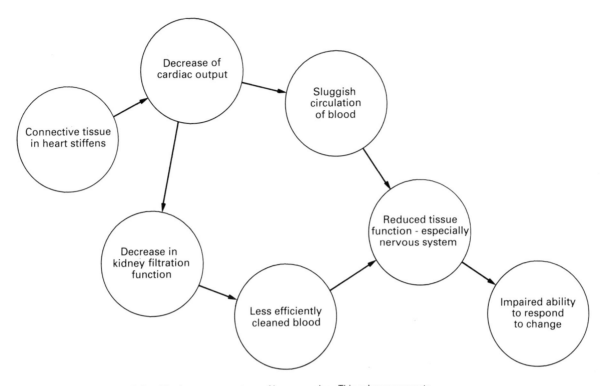

Figure 4.18 Possible inter-relationships between symptoms of human ageing. This scheme suggests a sequence of events which might follow recognised changes in connective tissue in the heart

identification of cross-linking between the protein molecules underlying both processes. This explanation was attractive for two reasons. First, it provided a means by which many of the disparate changes listed in Table 4.6 could be correlated (Fig.4.18), with those not included being due directly to cross-linking in connective tissues in other locations. Second, it suggested a possible strategy for the treatment of ageing. If cross-linking could be prevented or reversed then ageing could be counteracted. The evidence that mice fed on a minimal-calorie diet age more slowly and live longer is also interesting in this context. Break-down products of glucose are known to be cross-linking agents. The site of action of a low calorie intake seems to be the hypothalamus with its biological clock functions.

More recently the cause of ageing has been sought in the faulty copying of DNA prior to nuclear division or in the accumulation of errors in the DNA blueprint due to mutagenic agents. These are both time dependent and also give the explanation a genetic dimension. However, current evidence does not support either of these as the single cause

of ageing. It seems likely that all of the factors discussed could contribute to ageing and death but that a species possesses a genetic programme which determines its longevity. This programme may be thought of as controlling when particular genes are expressed. It is the expression of these genes late in the life cycle that is responsible for our present longevity and this has resulted from evolutionary selection by the weeding out of harmful genes that operate early in life. This still implies that ageing and death are due to 'harmful' genes. However, while we consider senescence as inevitable, we make a virtue of death. We explain it as a way of ridding society of the decrepit and frail to make way for the young and vigorous and so allow for evolutionary advance. This begs the question of why ageing has occurred in the first place. Accepting that ageing is basically a genetic phenomenon, future research into ageing is likely to be two pronged: first to delay ageing so that those surviving beyond 70 may do so in good physical and mental health until close to their death; and second, to genetically engineer a longer life span. The latter of these is a very controversial subject.

5 SOME ISSUES IN HUMAN GENETICS

GENE PROBES FIND HUNTINGTON'S DISEASE

American researchers have discovered a technique that may soon allow doctors to predict if people are carrying the gene for a lethal, inherited disease of the nervous system - Huntington's chorea.

This advance will pose major ethical questions about the use of such predictive tests. British doctors are split over whether they should introduce a test before a cure for Huntington's chorea is established.

This disease is unusual in that it results from a single, dominant form of a gene. If a person carries the defective form of the gene, he or she will die of the disease. But the process of degeneration does not start until middle age, so victims can have normal, healthy lives and bear children before they realise that they have the disease. If they have children then these offspring face a 50:50 risk of carrying the gene if one of the parents has a lethal version of the gene.

American researchers located the Huntingdon's gene by studying blood samples from two large families - one in the USA and one in Venezuela - that have a history of Huntington's chorea. They did this by using a length of human DNA called a 'marker'. The marker they used is called G8. In a series of experiments using certain types of enzymes that snip DNA into fragments, the marker was found to have a strong genetic linkage to the Huntington's gene. The G8 marker is already known to come from the fourth chromosome in the human genome of 23 pairs of chromosomes, and so the Huntington's gene must be on chromosome 4.

The American team investigated the degree to which the probe and gene are linked with the help of blood samples sent from Britain by Professor Peter Harper of the Welsh National School of Medicine. He has studied families in South Wales with histories of the disease. He has also sent samples that have been collected from similar families in East Anglia. These families have been studied by Dr Adrian Caro, a doctor who has devoted much of his career to Huntington's disease.

If a predictive test is found it will pose problems for doctors. Caro points to one difficulty he will face. He has a patient whose mother died of the disease; the patient therefore has a 50 per cent chance, and the son of this patient, has a 25 per cent chance, of developing the disease. If a predictive test shows that the patient definitely carries the gene, the chances of the son carrying the gene immediately jumps to 50:50. 'Do I tell him? What do I do?' he asks.

Another dilemma is whether or not to tell third parties, such as insurance firms and employers, of a patient's death sentence. Caro describes how many life assurance companies ask him, with the patient's consent, about the patient's medical history. He always asks for evidence of consent and demands to see the signature on the small print on insurance forms saying: 'I consent to the company seeking medical information from any doctor who at any time has attended me concerning anything which affects my physical or mental health'. 'Should I tell them that my patient will die in middle age?'

Similarly, he asks whether he is duty-bound to tell employers, and cites a recent case where the Royal Air Force asked him for details of a person who wanted to join and could be flying aircraft at a time when he unwittingly suffers from early symptoms of Huntington's - loss of memory and nervous twitches.

Another problem is prenatal diagnosis. A mother whose fetus has the gene could be offered an abortion; but it also means that she, or the father, also has the gene. The fetus could live quite healthily to the age of 40 or so. Marjorie Guthrie, the wife of the American folk singer, Woody, who died of Huntington's chorea, summed up his dilemma when, in a personal view of genetic counselling published in 1979, she wondered whether people would have preferred such a talented man (he inspired Bob Dylan) never to have existed.

In Britain, there are about 6000 sufferers of Huntington's chorea, and another 50 000 who either carry the gene but are too young to show symptoms, or are at risk and live under the threat of developing the disease with all its disturbing symptoms of nervousness, irritability, and dementia.

Doctors are deeply divided on the ethics of predictive tests. The patients themselves are unsure whether they want one. Harper found that just over half the people in a group of Welsh families at risk who were polled for their thoughts said they would take such a test if one existed.

■ INHERITANCE AND ENVIRONMENT

A person's appearance, metabolism, behaviour and all their other characteristics are determined by their genetic inheritance and by their environment. The characteristics (or traits), whether they are directly visible or whether they need tests to observe them, are called the person's *phenotype*. Their genetic make-up is called their *genotype*. You might think that when a baby is born, its phenotype is entirely determined by its genotype, because the environment has not yet affected it. But during the nine months before birth, the environment inside the womb can affect the baby's phenotype, as can the birth process itself. (See Table 4.4 for some examples of prenatal environmental factors affecting fetal development.)

Some phenotypic traits are determined entirely by the genotype. They are mostly features which have discontinuous variation, i.e. there are only a few distinct different versions of each characteristic. Blood group proteins and eye colour are examples. These cannot be changed during the lifetime of the person. Other phenotypic traits are influenced by the environment. These are mostly attributes which have continuous variation, like height, weight and skin colour. The environment cannot alter the genotype (except by increasing the rate of mutations, see later.) A person's genotype sets the potential limits of the characteristic, for example the tallest he could grow, or the lightest and darkest colours of her skin. After that, the environment that we experience determines our actual characteristics. The word environment includes all the influences on a person. If a child is well fed he should grow to his tallest potential; if another person is always in the sunshine she should get to her darkest potential. If children are stimulated, educated and encouraged their intelligence, skill and ability should develop towards their maximum potential.

In some situations it is known that a precise environmental factor is necessary for a certain genetic constitution to exert its effect. This knowledge is important in controlling the effects of some genetic diseases such as PKU (see below). The basic explanation of genetics and DNA is to be found in *Biology Advanced Studies - Genetics and Evolution*. Here we will note some important aspects of human genetics.

Where is the genotype located?

The genotype or genetic constitution of an individual is located in the chromosomes present in the nucleus of every cell of the body. The chromosomes are identical in every cell of our body, whether it is a brain cell, a muscle cell or a bone cell. The chromosomes appear to be the same in all people, but there are unique differences in their detailed chemical composition between different individuals. Only identical twins have chemically identical chromosomes.

Chromosomes can only be seen in cells which are dividing, and they have to be specially stained or illuminated and viewed with a microscope.

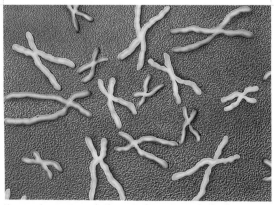

Human chromosomes in the metaphase stage of mitosis

1	2	3	4	5	6
7	8	9	10	11	12
13	14	15	16	17	18
19	20	21	22		X X

Figure 5.1 Karyotype of normal human female. Note how the 23rd pair consist of two X-chromosomes

A cytogeneticist arranges photographs of human chromosomes into a karyotype. Detection of any abnormalities in the number or structure of the chromosomes may give rise to the diagnosis of a defect in the individual (e.g. Down's Syndrome and some leukaemias)

Karyotypes

Once the chromosomes have been viewed they can be matched into pairs and laid out to show the individual pattern or *karyotype*. Figure 5.1 shows the karyotype of a normal human female.

1. How many chromosomes make up the normal human karyotype?

2. Are the chromosomes all different?

3. If not, what do you notice about the pattern of similarities?

4. The matching chromosomes of a pair are called homologous chromosomes. How many pairs of homologous chromosomes make up the karyotype?

Some people have different numbers of chromosomes from the usual 46. People suffering from Down's syndrome have an extra chromosome number 21, making a total of 47 instead of the usual 46. People with this condition have particular facial characteristics, are usually shorter and less intelligent than average, and tend to have weak hearts (Fig.5.2).

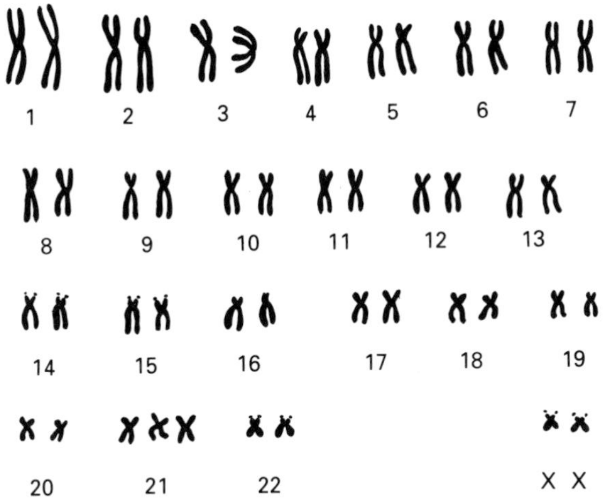

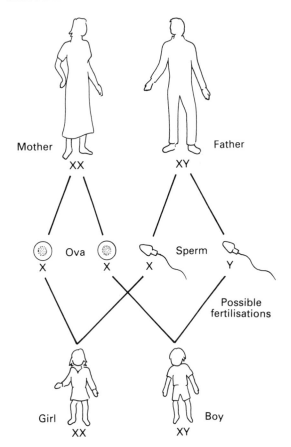

Figure 5.2 Karyotype of Down's syndrome female with an extra copy of chromosome 21

■ Sex determination

Q 5. How does the karyotype of a man differ from that of a woman? (Look at Figs.5.1 and 5.3)

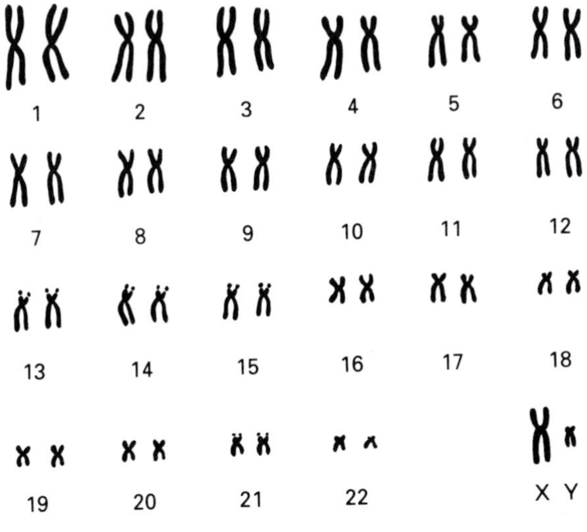

Figure 5.3 Karyotype of normal human male. Note how the 23rd pair consists of one X-chromosome and one Y-chromosome

The human karyotype consists of 22 matching pairs of chromosomes called autosomes, plus one pair of sex chromosomes. In females this pair match and are called XX. In males there is one X and a smaller Y chromosome. Females' cells also contain a tiny structure called a Barr body which is not in males' cells.

Some of the autosomes also contribute to sex determination, but except in rare exceptional individuals, the X and Y system overrides other determinants.

Figure 5.4 A genetic cross to explain sex determination

According to Fig.5.4 there is an equal chance of a boy or a girl being produced at each instance of fertilisation. Therefore you would expect an equal number of boys and girls to be born. However, world-wide figures show that more boys than girls are born, with the exact sex ratio varying between different populations. For example, in England and Wales in the 1960s, 105 boys were born to every 100 girls.

Condition	Sex chromosomes	Apparent sex	Syndrome	Incidence
Turner's syndrome	X (XO)	Female	Sterile, webbed neck, short, characteristic face	1 in 7000 births
Klinefelter's syndrome	XXY	Male	Sterile, very small testes, very tall	1 in 1000 births
	XYY	Male	Normal man	1 in 2000 births
	XXX XXXX XXXXX XXXY XXXXY XXXXXY	Female Female Female Male Male Male	Often have many physical and mental disabilities	

Table 5.1

There are some other conditions known to be due to specific extra chromosomes. Some syndromes (collections of particular signs and symptoms) are caused by unusual sex-chromosome constitutions as shown in Table 5.1.

Q 6. What decides whether a person is male or female? Is it the number of X chromosomes, or the presence or absence of Y chromosomes? Use the clues from Table 5.1 to discover the answer.

People with XYY chromosomes are normal men, mostly taller than average and most of whom are not aware of any unusual chromosome condition. At one time it was claimed that the XYY constitution contributed to criminal behaviour, based on statistics of this condition amongst the prison population compared to the population at large. Even if there is a slight statistical correlation, at least 96 per cent of XYY men do not behave in criminal ways so there is no basis for suspecting them any more than the average person.

■ GENES

Each chromosome carries many pieces of genetic information (genes) to code for all of a person's human and individual traits. The genetic code is in the form of the chemical DNA (deoxyribonucleic acid) making up the chromosomes. Each gene is a length of DNA, which occupies a particular position (locus) on a particular chromosome. Genes code for the production of specific proteins in cells. Many genes exist in two or more different versions. The different forms are called *alleles* of the gene. Each allele codes for a different variant of protein, or maybe for the absence of the gene's specific protein. If identical alleles occur at a locus on both homologous chromosomes, the person is *homozygous* for that gene. A person who is *heterozygous* for a particular gene has different alleles at that locus on each chromosome of the pair.

■ Blood groups

People vary in the proteins on their red blood cells. An individual may have protein A, or B, or both A and B, or neither; i.e. there are four different phenotypes of the ABO blood group system. For a blood transfusion or organ transplant to be successful, the donor's blood group must be compatible with that of the recipient. A 'foreign' protein of the system must not be transfused into a patient. If a foreign protein is put in (e.g. if AB blood was transfused into a group A patient), antibodies would react with the foreign protein, in this case B, and cause the red blood cells to stick together and block the blood capillaries.

Q 7. Which blood group can be transfused safely into any other person?

8. Which blood group can receive blood from any other person?

The system is genetically controlled by a locus on a particular chromosome pair. There are three possible alleles, I^A, I^B, I^O. A person has two alleles which may be the same or different.

Possible genotypes	Phenotype
$I^A I^A$	A
$I^A I^O$	A
$I^A I^B$	AB
$I^B I^B$	B
$I^B I^O$	B
$I^O I^O$	O

Table 5.2 ABO blood groups

Look at Figure 5.5 and Table 5.2 to help you to answer these questions.

Q 9. How many different genotypes are possible?

10. How many different phenotypes are possible?

11. Which people are homozygous and which are heterozygous?

12. What protein does allele I^A code for?

13. What protein does allele I^B code for?

14. What does allele I^O code for?

(a) Both parents are group B

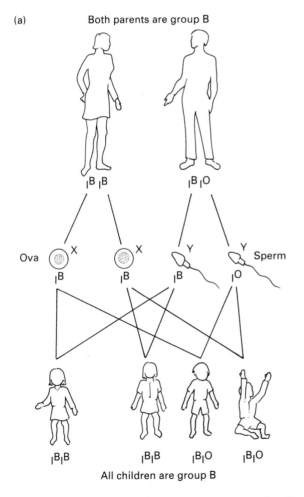

$I^B I^B$ $I^B I^O$

Ova   X   X   Y   Y Sperm

I^B I^B I^B I^O

$I^B I^B$ $I^B I^B$ $I^B I^O$ $I^B I^O$

All children are group B

(b) Both parents are group B

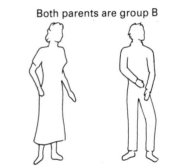

Children are either group B or group O

Figure 5.5 Copy diagram (b) and explain by adding to the diagram how these parents have children of group B and group O. What is the chance of one of their children being group O?

Tissue typing

The histocompatibility leucocyte antigen (HLA) system is a system of proteins on leucocytes (white blood cells) and in all tissues. For an organ transplant to be successful, the HLA proteins of the donor must match those of the recipient as closely as possible. Testing for a person's HLA group is called tissue typing. The system is controlled by genes at six loci which are all on chromosome number 6. At each of these loci there are many alleles possible as alternatives. This allows an enormous number of combinations, and hence an enormous number of phenotypes. The different types of protein are not equally common; the frequency varies between different populations. The more closely related people are, the more likely it is that their HLA antibodies are similar. The system also seems to determine susceptibility to certain diseases, e.g. juvenile diabetes and multiple sclerosis.

Sickle-cell genetics

Other loci control other blood protein variations. Muriel has normal haemoglobin, coded by several genes including alleles A and A at a certain locus. Her husband Michael has sickle-cell haemoglobin, coded by alleles S and S at the same locus. He suffers from sickle-cell anaemia.

Their son Junior has inherited one allele A from his mother and one allele S from his father, so he codes for both kinds of haemoglobin. He has sickle-cell trait, i.e. he carries the allele S. He is generally healthy as he has enough ordinary haemoglobin for normal activity.

Thalassaemia

Anna has all the normal haemoglobin alleles. Her husband Niko has an unusual allele at one of the loci controlling haemoglobin. He has the allele on both homologous chromosomes. They code for another kind of sickle cell haemoglobin and so he suffers from thalassaemia major, a severe and potentially fatal anaemia (see Figure 5.6).

Their daughter Anika inherited one normal allele from her mother and a thalassaemia allele from her father, so half her haemoglobin is the thalassaemia type. She has thalassaemia minor (a mild anaemia or asymptomatic condition).

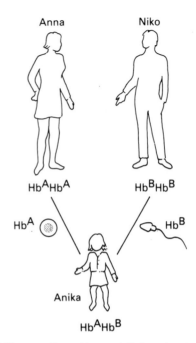

Figure 5.6 The normal form of haemoglobin is produced by the allele Hb^A and the homozygous sufferer (with thalassaemia major) would be $Hb^B Hb^B$ - many do not survive beyond childhood

Huntington's disease: a serious effect of a dominant allele

A serious example of a single-gene, dominant characteristic is the inherited disease Huntington's chorea (HC), the subject of the article at the beginning of this chapter. The great majority of people have a normal allele at the particular locus on both chromosomes number 4. About 5 people in every 100 000 in Britain have the HC allele on one chromosome.

Q 15. Peter and Pauline, both apparently normal, have two children Jessica and Stuart. When he was 35, Peter developed the symptoms of HC. Pauline remained well. Because HC is so rare, it is most unlikely that two people with the allele would marry so Pauline can assume she does not have it. What is the chance that their daughter Jessica has inherited HC?

16. What is the chance that their son Stuart has inherited HC?

17. What advice would you give to Jessica and to Stuart about getting married and having children?

■ Conditions due to recessive alleles

Many unusual human conditions are known to be due to a recessive allele, where the dominant allele of the gene codes for the normal condition. Some people (about 1 in 20 000) cannot make the dark coloured pigment called melanin in their bodies. These people (called albinos) have pale skin, white hair and pink eyes and their skin is susceptible to sunburn and skin cancer. Most albinos are homozygous for a certain recessive allele.

Albino person

Q 18. Two parents with normal colouring may have albino children if both parents are heterozygotes. If they have several children, would you expect them all to have albinism?

19. What would you expect about all the children of two albino parents?

A serious genetic disease which can easily be detected is phenylketonuria (PKU). A sample of blood is taken from new-born babies and then examined by a routine test.

About 1 in 20 000 white babies, but virtually no black babies will show a positive result. A child with PKU cannot breakdown phenylalanine from its diet in the normal way, so this amino acid and some abnormal products accumulate in the body causing severe mental retardation.

This is an example of the phenotype resulting from the interactive effects of both the genotype (PKU allele) and the environment (the diet). The genetic condition cannot be cured but the phenotypic effect can be prevented by controlling the diet. The child is given a diet very low in phenylalanine for the first few years, so that the chemicals are not present to damage the developing brain. For the rest of his or her life he or she can eat normal food. When a PKU carrier is pregnant she must resume the restricted diet in order to protect her baby's brain, whether or not the baby has inherited the disease. The disease is due to a recessive allele. Carriers of PKU (i.e. heterozygotes) can also be detected by a blood test which shows a high but not dangerous level of phenylalanine.

■ Cystic fibrosis

About 1 in 2000 white babies is born with cystic fibrosis (CF). This is another genetic disease which has recessive inheritance. The recessive allele is quite common in the population, with one person in every 22 being a heterozygous carrier.

Figure 5.7 shows the Mendelian principle of inheritance leading to a monohybrid ratio of three healthy children to one affected child (3:1). Note that 50 per cent of the progeny are carriers.

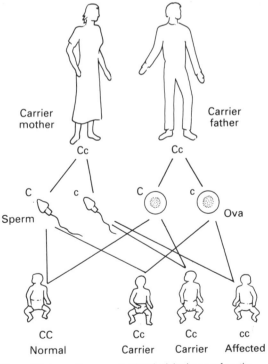

Figure 5.7 A genetic cross showing the inheritance of cystic fibrosis

John and Jennifer are normal healthy people whose daughter Sarah is normal. Then they had another baby, Robert, who was born with cystic fibrosis. He must be homozygous recessive for the cystic fibrosis gene.

Q 20. John looked at a diagram like the one shown in Figure 5.7 and said that he and Jennifer could have two more children without the risk of further cystic fibrosis sufferers, because only one in four children of an affected family has the disease. Was he correct?

21. If John and Jennifer have another child, what is the chance of it having cystic fibrosis?

The 3:1 ratio shows the chance of *each* child of a heterozygous couple being healthy or a CF sufferer, but in an average human family of a few children the ratio does not become evident. If you counted the children of hundreds of such families, the ratio would show up in the whole of that group.

The probability of John (a carrier) marrying a carrier of CF was about 1 in 500 if he married a white European woman. If he had married an Asian or African woman the chance would have been far smaller. If he had married a cousin, the chance of them both having the same CF genes would have been much higher.

■ INCIDENCE OF GENETIC DISEASES

About three thousand genetic diseases have been identified. Amongst the five million genes of every person, probably about eight are in the potentially hazardous form. (Every person is probably a heterozygous carrier for about eight of the three thousand serious or lethal genetic conditions.) For most of these diseases the harmful recessive allele is very much rarer in the population than the cystic fibrosis allele. Therefore the chance of breeding with someone who has one of the same recessive alleles is very unlikely.

The more closely related people are, the more likely it is that they have the same alleles. One in 30 Jews is a carrier of the Tay-Sachs allele, which is extremely rare in non-Jewish populations. One in 36 000 children of Jewish marriages is born with Tay-Sachs disease, characterised by deterioration of mental and motor function, blindness and the early death of the child.

A recessive condition called six-fingered dwarfism is very rare except amongst the Amish community of Pennsylvania. Here it is common due to intermarriage within a reproductively isolated community.

Close relatives who marry are more likely to have an albino child than are people who marry outside their family. In the United States, 0.1 per cent of marriages are between first cousins, but 8 per cent of all albinos result from first-cousin marriages.

■ SEX-LINKED CONDITIONS

Over 100 abnormal traits are known to be determined by genes located on the sex chromosomes. There are very few known on the Y chromosome; nearly all are on the X chromosome. Most of the sex-linked traits are determined by alleles at loci on the X chromosome for which there is no corresponding locus on the Y chromosome.

The inability to distinguish between the colours red and green is one condition inherited in X-linked pattern. It is quite common in males, affecting about eight per cent of white males, so there is a high chance that any school class contains at least one red-green colourblind boy. It is very rare in females for reasons to be explained later. A much more serious X-linked disorder is Duchenne muscular dystrophy (DMD) which shows up in early childhood with progressive muscle weakness and early death. Female carriers of muscular dystrophy suffer from muscular tiredness.

Muscular dystrophy. Child sufferer's of muscular dystrophy meet in the open air, outside a support centre with their parents, to take part in outdoor activities. Specially adapted wheelchairs, into which the body is strapped, provide body support and give each child mobility

Classical haemophilia (haemophilia A) is the best-known example of a sex-linked condition as it was inherited from Queen Victoria by several royal families of Europe. Haemophiliacs have blood which does not clot properly; they bruise easily and bleed excessively. There are various kinds of haemophilia. Classical haemophilia is caused by a deficiency of Factor VIII, essential in the clotting system. It is one of the oldest recognised genetic disorders as there are records in the Talmud from before the sixth century AD. The Jewish religious law exempted from circumcision any boy whose brother or cousin through the female line had bled excessively after circumcision. It did not exempt brothers from the same father but with a different mother. This shows that the rabbis at that time knew of the pattern of inheritance through female carriers, though of course they did not know the genetic cause.

A male with the X-linked allele for haemophilia is totally lacking in the ability to make Factor VIII. A female carrier has one normal allele which can code for Factor VIII, but her other (haemophilia) allele has some effect, such that she may have slightly impaired blood-clotting ability.

It is an oversimplification to say that the normal allele is totally dominant to the disease allele, but generally carriers are healthy and do not realise that they are carriers until they are specifically tested. It is extremely rare for a female to have a X-linked disease herself. She would have to be homozygous for the disease allele, i.e. she would have to be the daughter of an affected father and a carrier mother.

■ INHERITANCE OF CONTINUOUS VARIATIONS

The examples of inheritance discussed so far are examples of discontinuous variations which are determined by genes and are little influenced by the person's environment. Many are unusual conditions affecting very few people. Most human characteristics, however, show continuous variation. Height, weight, skin colour, hair colour, pulse rate and most other features do not fall into two or a few categories, but vary over a continuous range.

In most cases, a continuous variation is determined by several different genes at different loci on different chromosomes, each with several alleles. A person's height depends on separate genes which code for each enzyme which digests food and prepares the building materials for growth, for the rate at which calcium is deposited in the leg bones, for the production of growth hormone, etc. When different genes contribute to determining one phenotypic feature it is called *polygenic inheritance*.

We can also see continuous variation within a population for one particular characteristic, e.g. height. In any given population (for example, all the pupils in your school) there will be a few very tall people, a few very short people and the majority will be around an average height (see Figure 5.8).

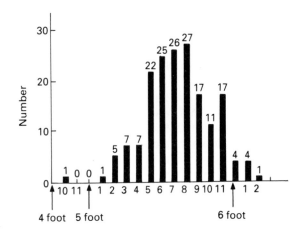

Figure 5.8 Continuous variation: A group of 175 soldiers were arranged in groups according to height (lower row of figures - in feet and inches). The number in each height group is shown above each bar

If you inherit the tall alleles of every 'height-determining' gene you will have the potential to grow very tall. If you inherit all the short alleles you will be short. If you have a mixture of 'short' alleles at certain loci and 'tall' alleles at other loci you will be of middle stature. Your genes will determine your potential height, but continuously varying characteristics are also affected by a person's environment. For example, a boy whose parents and ancestors were all tall may inherit the genetic potential for tallness. He will only attain the full height for which he is 'programmed' if he is well-nourished during childhood and does not suffer any serious accidents or diseases.

THE INHERITANCE OF INTELLIGENCE

There has been much discussion amongst scientists and the public about the relative influence of inheritance and environment on the level of a person's intelligence. This has been called the 'nature versus nurture' controversy (see Chapter 4 page 39). Both sets of factors seem to be influential. Intelligence is not a definable or measurable trait like height or even hair colour. What is intelligent behaviour in one situation, such as taking an IQ test or exam, may not be intelligent behaviour for survival in a jungle or desert. Without a valid criterion of 'intelligence', quantitative estimates of the contribution of genetics and the environment are valueless. It is important to know that to develop their intellectual, social and emotional skills children need a caring and stimulating environment in which to grow up.

CONGENITAL CONDITIONS

Any condition that a baby has when it is born is called a congenital condition. Some congenital disabilities (e.g. PKU, haemophilia) are clearly due to genes but others are due partly or wholly to environmental factors that the fetus has experienced before birth. The thalidomide tragedy of the 1960s showed one effect of a drug contributing to the fetal environment. Thousands of children in Britain and West Germany were born with arms and legs absent or deformed as a result of being exposed to thalidomide. This drug had been prescribed to their mothers during early pregnancy and it interfered with the fetal development. However, some women who took the drug at the same stage of pregnancy had normal babies, and sometimes these abnormalities occurred where no environmental factor could be identified. A number of drugs of medical or social use, and environmental factors due to the parents' occupations, are known to increase the incidence of congenital abnormalities. (See Table 4.4.)

SCREENING FOR GENETIC DISEASES

Although everyone possesses about eight potentially hazardous alleles, it would be neither feasible nor useful to screen us all for our genetic make-up. Screening for certain genetic diseases at birth (e.g. PKU and congenital hip dislocation) can identify sufferers and initiate treatment. Where a genetic disease is common, screening a population may be useful. In Italy carriers of thalassaemia have been identified by screening, and some Jewish populations have been screened for carriers of Tay-Sachs disease. Knowing that you are a carrier, you can make an informed decision about whom to marry and whether to have children. Genetic counselling may be useful where there is a family history of a genetic disease. A couple's genotypes for a particular condition can usually be inferred from their own symptoms and/or family pedigree. Chemical tests for proteins in blood, urine, and so on can confirm most such deductions. Advice on genetic matters is always given in terms of probability. John and Jennifer, in the example on page 67 have a 1 in 4 chance that their next child and any subsequent child will have cystic fibrosis.

Prenatal diagnosis of genetic disorders can be performed by amniocentesis, fetal blood sampling, ultrasound and fetoscopy. If a serious disorder is identified, the parents may wish to consider termination of the pregnancy.

MUTATION

Sometimes a child is born with a particular characteristic unlike that of either of its parents or family, and which could not be predicted by examining the family tree. About 1 in 10 000 people is an achondroplastic dwarf with short arms and legs but a normal sized trunk and head. Most dwarf children are born to normal parents with no history of dwarfism in their families. The condition arises by mutation. A mutation is a sudden change in the genetic material, which is then inherited in the changed form. In the case of achondroplasia, a 'normal' gene is incorrectly copied during gamete formation and becomes a 'dwarfism' allele. The dwarfism allele is dominant; achondroplastic dwarfs are heterozygotes. Probably homozygotes for this condition are not viable and they would die as very early embryos.

Q 22. Daisy is an achondroplastic dwarf. She married Daniel, also a dwarf. They had a dwarf child, Beth, and a normal child Thomas. Explain by a diagram the genetics of this family.

Some mutations consist of a change in the structure of a chromosome or set of chromosomes, involving many genes. Down's syndrome results from a chromosome mutation in the egg cell of the mother. Mutations occur spontaneously at a characteristic frequency for each gene. Certain chemicals including mustard gas, X-rays and other forms of radiation are known to increase the rate of mutation in some organisms. They are called mutagenic agents. They surely have a similar effect on the mutation of human genes but the evidence is limited.

■ THE PROSPECTS FOR HUMAN GENETICS

Cloning human beings and other genetic engineering projects to produce Supermen and Superwomen is the stuff of science fiction. However, substituting a 'normal' allele for a 'disease' allele in a human embryo is a prospect for the not too distant future.

Already, gene therapy has helped some patients. One of the first such research programmes treated a patient lacking a single gene responsible for an enzyme (ADA) crucial for her immune system. Through an injection, millions of copies of the missing gene, carried by a virus, were inserted into her body to code for the enzyme. Researchers in other groups are developing a gene therapy for cystic fibrosis sufferers. They are investigating the possibility of injecting, direct into the patients' bronchial tubes and lungs, the 'normal' allele to over-ride the effect of the cystic fibrosis allele. Already this has proved successful in experimental mice. Yet another research group has developed a method, currently being tested on experimental animals, as a new approach to treating cancer. Malignant melanoma (a skin cancer) is the first target, but the technique may be extended to treat other cancers. It involves injecting a piece of DNA directly into a cancer cell. This DNA is the gene which codes for the protein called interleukin 2, which will switch on the body's own defense mechanism to reject the tumour.

Genetic engineering, in which a particular gene is extracted from a cell of one species and inserted it into a cell of another species, is already having notable successes. Bacteria, into which the appropriate human genes are transferred, can make 'human' chemicals. This technique is already being used to make insulin, interferon and human growth hormone for medical use. Gene transfer techniques may help to provide organs for transplanting into patients. Current research involving the transfer of human genes into pigs may result in pig's hearts which can be transplanted into humans without fear of rejection.

The case study at the beginning of this chapter indicates one use of DNA markers and the ethical dilemma it is posing to doctors. The so-called DNA fingerprinting technique is used to identify particular genes and alleles by analysis of samples of blood and other tissues. This can indicate relationships between individuals in cases of unsure parentage. For example, it is being used to identify the biological families of children separated from their parents by former military activities in Argentina (see page 66 of *Biology Advanced Studies - Biochemistry*).

A team of scientists is currently mapping the human *genome*; they are attempting to identify the locus of every human gene. Locating the genes for all normal and abnormal conditions would appear to open up possibilities for diagnosing, preventing and treating genetic problems. But who can define what is normal and what abnormal, what is desirable and what undesirable in human genetic programming? The cost of this research is enormous! Some people see huge potential profit in the biotechnology of using this information in the pharmaceutical industry. There is much debate on the ethics of patenting knowledge gained in human genome research. Can it be possible to patent the instructions that we each carry in every one of our cells? A quote from the seventeenth century poet John Milton is very relevant to the contemporary situation: 'Knowledge enormous makes a God of me'. With the God-like knowledge of the blueprints for humans comes the need for a God-like wisdom and responsibility.

6 HUMANS AS SOCIAL ORGANISMS

■ SOCIALISATION

Humans are born in a very helpless state. A baby inherits the physical characteristics and mental potential of the human species, evolved over millions of years. In the individual the potential has to develop by maturation. However, to become a functional member of human society, he or she has to learn the culture of the human species and of his or her particular community. Humans have a long childhood, dependent on their parents and the whole society, during which this learning process (*socialisation*) can occur. From prehistoric times, children must have been introduced to the behaviour and skills necessary to co-operate in their tribal group. Most socialisation, even today, occurs informally by the child following the example of its parents and elders.

Homo sapiens is unique in that many characteristics that define our species, namely language, tool-making, command of fire, art and spirituality are not handed on genetically. They are handed on socially. We have to learn to be human.

Some characteristics of humans: language, spirituatity, craftwork and literature

Different cultures and races

■ VARIATION WITHIN THE HUMAN SPECIES

People all over the world share the same physical and social attributes that define them as human. However, there is some variation between people in both their physical and cultural characteristics.

Q 1. How many races are represented in the photographs on pages 72 and 73?

2. What criterion did you use to decide the answer to question 1, in other words, how can we tell a person's race?

3. If you used a criterion for deciding a person's race, is it a biological criterion?

4. In your own class or group, what race does each person consider themselves to be or belong to? Or do they think that race is not a meaningful term?

There are no 'right answers' to these questions because the word 'race' is and has been used differently by different people in different contexts. Perhaps you decided that all the people in the picture are members of one 'human race'. The human species is clearly *polymorphic* (shows variation) in many characteristics, but many people believe that there is no biological justification for thinking of the human species as consisting of different races. The similarities between all people are overwhelmingly greater than the differences between them. The differences within one 'racial group' may be greater than the differences between two individuals of different 'racial groups'. If the word 'race' has any meaning in a biological sense, it applies to populations and not to individuals. We must examine the evidence for these points of view, while considering the biology of differences between human populations.

■ Variation in skin colour

People often associate race with skin colour. You may have identified people in the picture or in your group as being 'black' or 'white'. These words are often used to describe groups of people without really applying them to the colour of individuals' skin. People who describe themselves as black may in fact be paler than others who describe themselves as white. In whichever way the words are used in a social sense, skin pigmentation is one observable biological variation within the human population. This is a continuous variation, with an infinite number of shades and tones, not a discontinuous variation into two categories of black and white. As with many continuous variations, the visible appearance (phenotype) is caused not only by the genes, but also by the environment of the individual (e.g. exposure to sunlight or a sunbed).

Scientists have sought evidence for the origin and distribution of the variation in human skin colour, and suggested hypotheses to explain it.

The genus *Homo* probably evolved in tropical Africa and the earliest men and women were possibly darkly pigmented. Of course, fossil evidence cannot confirm this. Dark skin would have provided camouflage and protection from large carnivores. Also the pigment, melanin, absorbs ultraviolet radiation, preventing its carcinogenic effects and preventing the formation of excess vitamin D which would be toxic. As groups of people migrated further from the Equator, lighter-skinned individuals would have been at a selective advantage where less sunlight was available. They would be able to use the available sunlight to synthesise the vitamin D necessary for health without the risk of an excess. Dark skinned people would be at a disadvantage in not being able to make enough vitamin D in the poor sunlight. At that time the human population was sparsely distributed in reproductively isolated groups.

Gradual natural selection within each environment would account for the distribution of skin colours indicated in Fig.6.1.

In general the most darkly pigmented people live closest to the Equator and are exposed to the greatest concentration of sunlight, though in fact little light penetrates dense Equatorial forests where some of the darkest people originate. Although skin colour is an obvious variation, it is correlated, to some extent, with other superficial characteristics, associated with groups of people from various parts of the world.

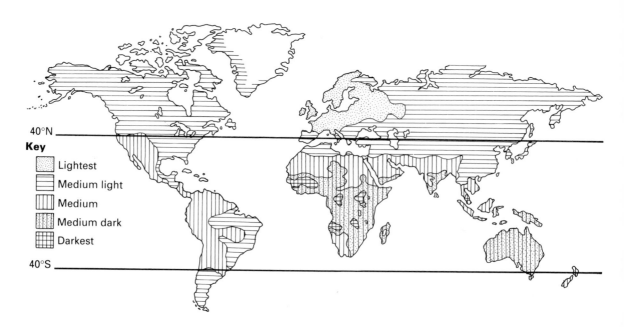

Figure 6.1 Skin colour distribution before 1492 AD

Key

- Lightest
- Medium light
- Medium
- Medium dark
- Darkest

40°N

40°S

■ Differences are skin-deep

Q 5. Look at the people in this picture who had come together from various parts of the world to attend a conference. Try to guess what country each person comes from. You may think that this is a trick question, because a person of any appearance may live anywhere in the world, but you can be fairly sure of their family origin within the past few generations and so identify them as Chinese, African, European and so on.

6. What features vary between people of these different groups?

To answer question 6 you will have thought of obvious features that we can see, such as the: colour of skin, hair, eyes; texture of hair; shape of folds over the eyes; shape of nose and lips.

These are all surface features of the body, at the interface between the body and its environment. The size of the surface area in relation to the mass of the body is another feature which shows continuous variation and which may have arisen as an adaptation to a range of climates. Different general body shape and distribution of fat had different selective advantages in different

environments, and they contribute to differences between certain groups of people.

Look at Fig.6.2 below. The tall slim Sudanese has a large surface area from which to lose excess heat, whereas the shorter and fatter Inuit has a relatively smaller surface area which loses less heat. These individuals are fairly representative of their isolated populations, but you may think it unreliable to generalise from individuals. You may be able to think of other explanations for their respective shapes related to the lifestyles of these two people.

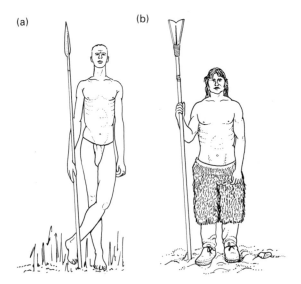

Figure 6.2 The body of the Sudanese (a) would be ill adapted to the Artic where the Inuit (b) is well adapted, and vice versa

The anatomical and biochemical features inside the body do not vary between groups in such a consistent pattern. In other words, biological racial characteristics are only skin-deep. They evolved in the early days of the human spread around the world. They evolved in relation to adaptation to different environments; adaptations of skin features in contact with the environment which were favourable in that particular environment were selected. Variations of internal parts, on the whole, were not subject to environmental selection pressures.

Sunday morning in an Amish village

■ EVOLUTION OF VARIATIONS

Evolution, that is the change in frequency of a particular variation within a population, may occur if that population becomes reproductively isolated from other populations of the species. The same geographical factors that isolate animal and plant populations have isolated human groups. The ocean isolated the Australian Aborigines until 200 years ago, and frozen Arctic wastes isolated the Inuit people. In South America many small tribes were isolated by dense rain forests.

Human groups can also be reproductively isolated by political, religious and cultural factors. In South Africa, until 1990, the law forbade marriage between black and white people. In the USA there are a number of religious sects (e.g. the Dunkers and the Amish) which have married only within their sect for the past 200 years.

Some of the evolution which occurs in isolated populations is adaptive by *natural selection* of the favourable variations in that environment. In small isolated populations, however, evolution also occurs by chance due to *genetic drift*. If there are only a few people with a certain characteristic, by chance they may have a lot of children, even if that characteristic does not make them more successful or attractive. By chance all those with another feature may die without children. In a large population it is far less likely that all the people with one variant will be wiped out by random chance.

■ BLOOD DIFFERENCES

Look again at your answers to the questions on page 73. Are there any internal, physiological or biochemical characteristics that people associate with different races? Sometimes people refer to 'white blood' and 'black blood' and suggest that a child of a black mother and white father has mixed blood. Of course everyone has red blood. There are several different proteins which can be identified from blood samples. Each protein has two or three alternative forms - each shows discontinuous variation.

Name	Blood group	Rhesus factor	[Genotype]
Brian	A	Rh⁻	Hb AA
Nasreen	AB	Rh⁺	Hb AA
Linda	O	Rh⁺	Hb AS
Chang	B	Rh⁺	Hb AA
Anna	O	Rh⁺	Hb AA

Table 6.1 The blood proteins of the people shown on page 73

Table 6.1 shows polymorphism of various proteins in human blood, but the blood proteins of an individual person do not correlate with their skin colour or any other characteristic. Blood proteins are determined by a person's genes (see page 64) and cannot be affected by the environment in which the person lives. The gene which determines the ABO blood group polymorphism exists as three alleles I^A, I^B and I^O.

	I^A (%)	I^B (%)	I^0 (%)
World-wide	22	16	62
Congo Pygmies	23	22	55
South American Indians	8	0	92
Australian Aborigines	30	2	68
Dunkers	38	2	60
Germans	29	7	64
North Americans (not native)	26	4	70

Table 6.2 Different populations have different frequencies of the blood group alleles

The frequency of the blood group alleles in a population can be calculated from the incidence of the different blood groups. The alleles are not equally distributed throughout the world, as shown in Table 6.2. These are statistical patterns. You could not assign a person to one of these groups just on the basis of their blood group. No one allele exists 100% in one racial group. The I^B allele is very rare in the South American Indian, Australian Aborigine, Basque (in Spain and France) and Irish populations, but these people do not appear to belong to the same racial group by other criteria. The Dunker sect (see page 76) have frequencies of alleles similar to those of Polynesian populations and quite different from the general population of the USA or of Germany where their ancestors came from.

Q 7. How do you think the Dunker pattern has evolved over only 200 years?

Another blood protein whose frequency varies between populations is the rhesus factor. This is genetically controlled by a number of alleles whose frequencies vary between Caucasoid, African and Mongoloid populations. Rh-negative blood is very rare amongst Africans and is most frequent in whites. Nearly all Africans have a blood protein given the name 'Duffy' but only three per cent of whites have it. However, a protein given the name 'Auberger' exists in different forms in every racial group, with no difference in the range of variation from population to population.

The pattern of variation does not enable us to identify races by blood groups, but the distribution of the groups can give some indication of the isolation or migration of populations in the past.

Is there any significance of blood-group distributions in different populations to explain how they may have come about? There is some evidence of correlation between particular blood groups and a tendency to certain ulcers or cancers, or a resistance to certain infections. For example the anti-A antibody (in blood O or B) seems to be effective against the virus which causes smallpox. However it is not clear how these correlations could be significant in blood group distributions.

■ Sickle-cell

Haemoglobin is a polymorphic blood protein, certain variants of which cause sickle-cell anaemia and thalassaemia. At first consideration, it might seem that sickle-cell anaemia is a racial marker as it affects 'blacks' of African descent but not white northern Europeans. (The disease and its inheritance are described on page 66.)

The geographic distribution of sickle-cell alleles in Africa, Arabia and Southern Europe, is shown in Figure 6.3. Children homozygous for the sickle-cell allele have sickle-cell anaemia and tend to die young. Children with sickle-cell trait (i.e. heterozygotes) survive, and so do people homozygous for the normal allele. However, in malarial areas, sickle-cell trait provides the heterozygotes with an advantage. The malaria parasites cannot grow well in the blood cells of a person with sickle-cell trait, so these people have some protection from the potentially fatal disease, malaria. People with usual haemoglobin do not have this protection from malaria.

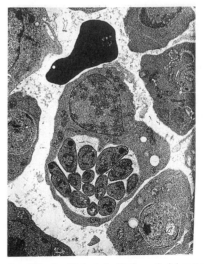

A red blood cell infected with the malarial parasite

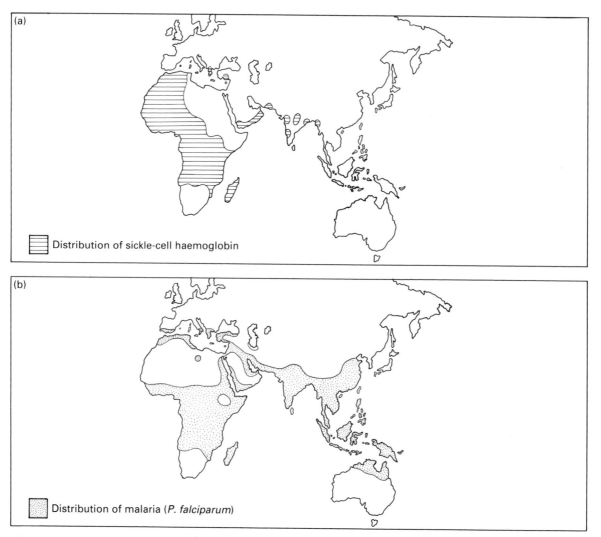

(a)

Distribution of sickle-cell haemoglobin

(b)

Distribution of malaria (*P. falciparum*)

Figure 6.3 The distribution of sickle-cell alleles and malaria

The 'black' population of the USA and Britain are mainly descendants of people taken from West Africa in the slave trade.

Sickle-cell disease occurs in these populations but in a smaller proportion than in West Africa. About 20 per cent of West Africans, but only about 10 per cent of Afro-Americans and Afro-British carry the sickle-cell allele.

Sickle-cell protein occurs mainly in African people, but also in people of Southern European and Arabic ancestry. It existed as an adaptation to particular environmental conditions and is eliminated by natural selection where the environmental conditions are different.

■ OTHER GENETIC DISEASES

Thalassaemia is another form of sickle-cell disease which occurs in populations of Mediterranean and Asian origin.

Several other genetic diseases, involving abnormal versions of particular proteins, are distributed differently in different racial populations. For example, Tay-Sachs disease is about a hundred times commoner in Jewish births than amongst non-Jews in the United States. Cystic fibrosis and PKU affect white people but are very rare amongst blacks and Orientals.

■ PROTEIN VARIATION

About 150 different genetically coded proteins have been studied. About 75 per cent of these are *monomorphic* proteins - they are identical in all human individuals. The other 25 per cent are polymorphic. Considering these proteins, there is far more variation between individuals within a local population, tribe or nation than between major 'races'. The genetic difference between one Spaniard and another, or between one Masai and another is 85 per cent of all human variation. Only 15 per cent of human variation in these proteins relates to differences between groups, and only half of that refers to differences between major 'races'.

■ IS RACE A MEANINGFUL CONCEPT?

In the nineteenth century and before, the word 'race' was used in many different ways, to mean all of humanity, a nation or just a family. When Darwin's theory of evolution emerged in the middle of the nineteenth century, biologists began to refer to different forms of animals within a species as 'races'. In the 1940s, studies in population genetics made it clear that such 'races' were in no way consistent between generations, and the word *morph* came to be applied to different forms. It was realised that different local populations of animals and plants do not differ from each other absolutely, but only in the relative frequency of different characteristics, as the distribution of human blood groups illustrates.

Biologically, 'race' came to be defined as a population of varying individuals, mating among each other, and different from other populations in average proportions of various genes. So race applies to populations, not individuals. No individual is typical of its race, as the essence of the definition lies in the notion of variation. By this definition, any local interbreeding population is a race. It could be an isolated mountain village population or a religious sect who rarely marry outside their community. It does not correspond with the idea of a small fixed number of races as are described in some older textbooks. One such list of races consists of: Asiatic, Indian, African, European, Australian Aborigine, Melanesian, Micronesian, Amerindian, Polynesian.

Ashley Montagu, an anthropologist who wrote *Statement on race* in 1957, argued that the biological concept of race is inappropriate to apply within the human species for the various reasons mentioned here. He regarded culture as the major factor in the development and unique adaptation of humans in contrast to other animals.

Unlike any other animal species, *Homo sapiens* has been able to colonise the whole world, because of the human ability to co-ordinate brain and hand to control the environment. In the early days of their migration, humans had limited control of the environment and biological adaptation was important. As cultural evolution progressed and people developed more control over their environment, the human body's immediate surroundings have become more consistent in all parts of the world. Clothes, houses and vehicles have made the physical differences between people less relevant in an adaptive biological sense.

With modern travel and migration and a more universal lifestyle, many families are being established with parents from different original populations. Because people from all the different population groups are marrying and having families, the biological definition of races as reproductively isolated breeding groups does not apply to humans. This is one reason for saying that 'race', as applied to people, is not a scientifically valid concept.

There are various myths about race. A racist claim is that there are major inherited differences in temperament, mental abilities, energy and so on between human groups. There is no scientific evidence for this. Some people assume that political, cultural, linguistic and religious differences are biologically determined. There is no scientific evidence for this either. Groups of people may wish to maintain particular customs, culture, religion or a way of life on the basis of their ethnic origins. This is a social matter and not a biological one.

CHAPTER 7

BEHAVIOUR - ASPECTS OF HEALTH, SEX AND GENDER

Homo sapiens is the most recent, and only surviving member of the genus *Homo*. That no new species has yet evolved may be due to a number of factors:

(i) Lack of time - *speciation* is a long-term process in a species with a long generation time.

(ii) Lack of isolation - either geographical or behavioural.

(iii) A move away from biological evolution to cultural evolution.

We consider our species to be the peak of the evolutionary process; but what of the future evolution of our species? The processes of natural selection are usually too slow to be observed. However, changes in behaviour have been noted and Professor Jean Rostand has speculated that twenty-first century *Homo sapiens* would be:

A strange biped capable of:
• self-reproduction without males
  (like the greenfly);
• fertilising its female at long distances
  (like the nautilus);
• growing from cuttings
  (like the earthworm);
• postponing implantation
  (like the badger);
• developing outside its mother's body
  (like the kangaroo);
• hibernating
  (like the dormouse);
• extending its lifespan
  (to rival that of the giant tortoise).

Perhaps we should consider some of these points and some other aspects of behaviour as well as the social implications. A significant change in British society came with the Representation of the People Act, 1918. At that time women over 30 gained the right to vote and finally, in 1928, women were given equal voting rights to men.

The reasons for this change in society usually include:

• the vital contribution made by women to the First World War (1914-1918). By 1918 almost five million women were in employment - many in jobs previously held only by men. Thousands served at the front, often in field hospitals.

• the reaction to the sexual morality of the Victorian middle class. This cast women in the passive, docile, obedient wifely role, innocent of passion and therefore uninterested in their own sexual fulfilment.

• the work of Sigmund Freud at the same time had heightened awareness of the psychological importance of human sexuality.

At this time there was also a fundamental change in society's attitudes to sexuality and the roles of the sexes. The pioneering work of Marie Stopes, whose first birth control clinic was established in 1923 led to further progress. That is not to say that she invented contraception. Records of contraception go back as far as a papyrus 'prescription' dating from 1850 BC for a copper intrauterine device. Almost every culture and civilisation has left records of its own methods of contraception. However, Stopes pointed the way to the breaking of the link of inevitability between sex and reproduction. The 'break' did not follow immediately. What Marie Stopes did was to begin to educate people, but especially women. With the refinement of traditional devices for greater effectiveness and, in particular the development of oral contraceptives in the 1950s the stage was set for a sexual revolution in contraception.

How can another woman make you pregnant?

Just by talking to you. And giving you bad advice.
Too many women risk getting bad advice about contraception because they'd rather listen to friends than go to a clinic or a doctor. No wonder there are 120,000 unwanted babies born in Britain every year.
No matter if you're young or old, married or single, you can get help and advice that is friendly, private, and above all, accurate, from your doctor or local family planning clinic.   The Health Education Council
You can find your local clinic under 'Family Planning' in the telephone directory or Yellow Pages. Or write to: The Health Education Council, 78 New Oxford Street, London WC1A 1AH

We have come to accept the terms contraception and family planning and some assume that they mean the same. However, the definition of the word 'family' has become very confused during the latter half of the twentieth century. No definition would satisfy everyone but 'a small social unit involving adults and children bonded by mutual affection' might prove acceptable to most people.

In 1967 the United Nations International Conference on Human Rights accepted unanimously the proposition that family planning is a basic human right. That declaration signed by leaders of 30 countries, representing 40 per cent of the world's population, includes the following words:

> *"We believe that the great majority of parents desire to have the knowledge and means to plan their families; that the opportunity to decide the number and spacing of children is a basic human right.*
> *We believe that the objective of family planning is the enrichment of human life, not its restriction; that family planning, by assuring greater opportunity to each person, frees man to attain his individual dignity and reach his full potential*

Q 1. In what ways do you think family planning can benefit individual people, and the world community as a whole?

The declaration (above) suggests the following benefits:
(i) Globally it could limit population growth at least until we are better able to cope with it.
(ii) In some parts of the world it could help to limit the ravages of famine and disease.
(iii) Individually it could:
• reduce the number of unwanted children.
• reduce the risk to a woman of ill-health due to constant child-bearing.
• reduce the need for abortion.
• reduce stress by freeing the sexual expression of love from the fear of pregnancy.
• increase opportunities for the achievement of full human potential.

IUD (the intrauterine device)
This is a small device, made of plastic with copper, put into the woman's womb by a doctor. Once in place it works for several years and stops any fertilised egg from settling there. Not a first choice method for young women.

STERILISATION

This form is a very effective, permanent form of family planning if you're absolutely sure you don't want any more children.
Vasectomy (male sterilisation). This involves a minor operation, in which the tubes carrying the sperm to your penis are cut and tied. Vasectomy doesn't affect your sex life. You still enjoy sex and climax, but your semen no longer contains sperm.
Female sterilisation. This means that the tubes carrying the egg to the womb are cut and blocked. It's not as simple as vasectomy because the tubes are harder to reach. The woman still has periods, still enjoys sex and climaxes, but she cannot conceive.

A WOMAN'S GUIDE
TO BIRTH CONTROL

THE CAP OR DIAPHRAGM

These are different types of thin rubber dome. Your partner (or you) places the cap insie her vagina before intercourse. The idea is to stop sperm getting into her womb. It must be used with a sperm-kiling cream, jelly, pessary, foam or film to be effective, but the same cap can be used again and again.

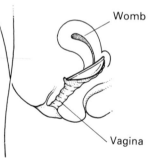

Womb

Vagina

This method may also give some protection against cancer of the cervix. If you have a steady relationship with your partner, maybe you can go along too when she has her cap or diaphragm fitted.

NATURAL METHODS

With these, you avoid your partner's fertile time each month. But you may very much want intercourse during the highly fertile days. If you and your partner prefer natural family planning you could both work out very carefully and accurately when her fertile days are, and show sexual feelings in other ways, or use a condom at that time. You could also go with her to a special teacher to learn how to use this method.

THE PILL

This prevents the woman's body from releasing a new egg each month. So no matter how many sperm enter the woman, pregnancy cannot occur. The pill is very effective, but some women have side-effects. So discuss this before deciding it's the best method for you both. Your partner (and you) can find out about possible side-effects from the doctor who prescribes the pill, and about the different kinds of pill available.

THE CONDOM

This is the most effective birth control that you can use yourself. It's made of thin rubber, and unrolls to fit over your erect penis. Pinch the air out of the closed end, before rolling the condom on with the flat part of your fingers (nails can damage the rubber). Your partner can put the condom on for you as part of loveplay.
It's important to put the condom on before intercourse, not just before you climax. (Remember all that sperm!) Also, to hold the condom in place around the penis when withdrawing, to avoid spilling sperm. Use a condom only once, then dispose of it carefully.
Condoms are sensitive and easy to use. You can get your condoms free from a family planning clinic (family doctors don't prescribe them), or you can buy them from chemists, garages, record shops, some supermarkets, slot machines or by mail order. Reliable condoms have a 'Kitemark' on the pack. The condom can help protect you and your partner against some sexually transmitted diseases, including HIV infection (important for safer sex). It may protect women against cancer of the cervix (neck of the womb).

THE SPONGE

This is soft and circular, and made of polyurethane foam. In one size, it already contains spermicide to provide 24 hours' contraceptive protection. It's put into the vagina anytime from a few seconds to as long as 24 hours before intercourse. After use the sponge is thrown away.

INJECTABLE CONTRACEPTION

With this method, a hormone is injected into a muscle, and released very slowly in the body over many weeks to stop egg release. It should only be offered to women who can't use other methods.

Figure 7.1 Adapted from a Family Planning Association Leaflet

It could be argued that readily available contraception has its disadvantages too. Before considering these, however, a review of the methods of contraception currently available will be helpful. The leaflet (Fig.7.1) provides a summary of these, in a form in which its author, the Family Planning Association (FPA), seems to be implying that men still have to be persuaded of their joint responsibility for contraception.

Q 2. If you look at magazines or books which deal with currently available methods of contraception, it is interesting to note that the text no longer includes reference to 'withdrawal' as a method of contraception. What reasons can you suggest for this deliberate omission?

Table 7.1 compares contraceptive methods for reliability and advisability. Interestingly the FPA leaflet shows only two established male forms of contraception - the condom and vasectomy. Whilst, in recent years, a great deal of research and development has gone into female contraception we might wonder what has been happening to male contraception! Two recent developments indicate some progress in this direction.

The male 'pill' is undergoing trials of effectiveness and acceptability as part of a world-wide project by the World Health Organisation. 'Pill' is not an accurate description, as the technique involves injection. It is called the 'pill' to highlight the use of hormones in parallel with the female pill. Its use of the male hormone testosterone reduces the sperm count to an ineffective level. The first clinical trials in Britain were very successful and a limited survey of public opinion indicated that almost 50 per cent of men welcomed the prospect of a male pill. However, the bad news is that this development has come at a time when large pharmaceutical companies are becoming wary of investment in new projects. This is because of the risks and high costs of court action in respect of unforeseen side-effects.

Method	Effectiveness	Comments
Sterilisation	100%	No further cost and usually irreversible
21 day pill	100%	Prescription reliable if used properly but the 21 day pill and 28 day pill may lead to weight increase and in some cases thrombosis
Mini-pill 28 day	99.8%	
Morning after pill	Probably 99-100%	
Intra-uterine device (IUD) (loop, coil)	98%	Only really suitable for women who have had children but only needs a check-up annually
Female diaphragm, cap	97%	Generally reliable when used with spermicide cream
Male condom, sheath	88%	Also gives some protection against STD and HIV - readily available. Some loss of sensitivity
Spermicide	Not reliable alone	Simple to use but not effective on its own
Rhythm method	Generally unreliable	Only method available to some religious groups

Table 7.1 Comparison of currently available methods of contraception. Figures for reliability vary considerably depending on their source. They should be considered comparatively rather than absolutely

A reversible vasectomy, in contrast, has the virtues of simplicity and of direct application to the global need as well as to the individual one.

Switch-back vasectomy heralded as breakthrough

A REVERSIBLE vasectomy method likely to revolutionise male contraception has been developed by the World Health Organisation. The new sterilisation technique, currently undergoing trials in China, should be ready for marketing in two to three years.

The method... involves injecting the two sperm ducts with liquid silicone rubber which hardens into a plug, stopping the passage of sperm. Trials have shown the plug is easily removable through a small puncture in the skin not big enough to require a stitch.

It is hoped the new method will fill a huge market for men who want to take responsibility for contraception, but are reluctant to opt for permanent sterilisation in case they remarry or lose a child...

Because it does not involve surgery, it is hoped the reversible plug will also prove acceptable to men in Islamic and African countries with spiralling population levels who have cultural objections to surgical vasectomy or to using condoms.

Two further developments in the field of contraception will put into perspective the social and moral complexity of the issues we are considering. 'Birth control by vaccination' makes a controversial headline if you consider the origin and subsequent use of vaccination as a preventative against infectious disease. However, using the same principles, researchers in Australia have made a vaccine against human chorionic gonadotrophic hormone whose activity is essential to pregnancy. Without it a fertilised egg will be expelled from the body during menstruation. At present re-vaccination is needed every six months but it seems likely that continued research will result in a vaccine whose effects are longer lasting. Its supporters expect it to be in general use within five to ten years and say it could replace the pill as the most popular form of contraception by the turn of the century. Table 7.2 shows what we choose to use currently.

Contraceptive method	% use
Pill	28
Condom (sheath)	13
Sterilisation (female)	11
Sterilisation (male)	10
IUD (loop or coil)	6
Withdrawal	4
Diaphragm (cap)	1
Safe period (rhythm)	1
Spermicides	1
No contraception	25

Table 7.2 Choice of contraception currently made in Britain

Q 3. The pill is less commonly used now than it was in the early 1970s. Can you suggest what could explain this decline?

4. It is expected that the popularity of the condom will increase. Can you suggest an explanation for this prediction?

The 'morning-after' pill is already available. As its name suggests it does not necessarily prevent fertilisation but probably works by preventing implantation. This brings into focus two issues raised in Chapter 4.

Q 5. What is the exact definition of 'conception'?

6. Are methods such as the 'morning after' pill, vaccination and the IUD forms of contraception or means of abortion?

With this picture of modern contraception we can return to the possible disadvantages of its universal availability. Criticisms that have been made, which are largely traceable to the introduction of the contraceptive pill, include:

(i) It could encourage greater sexual experimentation especially amongst the young. This could result in:
• increased risks of unwanted pregnancies in girls and young women (Table 7.3) and therefore increased numbers of abortions (Fig.7.2).
• increased promiscuity leading to greater risks of the spread of sexually transmitted diseases (STD - see Table 7.5).

Age in years	14	15	16	17	18	19
Conception rate *	6.0	20.7	46.0	68.7	86.5	99.8

Table 7.3 The number of teenage pregnancies in 1990 (England and Wales). * Rate indicates the number of pregnancies per 1000 of the age group

Age group	Rate of conception (per 1000 females in age group)		Abortions (per 1000 females) in age group)
13 - 15	1979	7.5	4.2
	1984	8.6	4.8
	1989	9.4	4.9
16	1979	40.6	17.2
	1984	41.9	18.7
	1989	46.0	19.5
18	1979	84.8	22.1
	1984	77.9	22.5
	1989	86.5	28.7

Table 7.4 Data from Figure 7.2

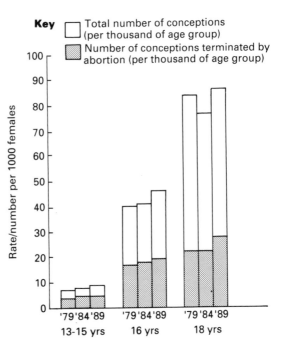

Key
□ Total number of conceptions (per thousand of age group)
▨ Number of conceptions terminated by abortion (per thousand of age group)

Figure 7.2 The number of teenage abortions in 1979, 1984 and 1984 (England and Wales)

Condition		16-19 year olds	Total (under 25 year old)	Total (all ages)
Infectious syphilis	M	5	45	222
	F	7	45	113
Post-pubertal uncomplicated gonorrhea	M	1328	5266	10925
	F	1891	4277	6113
Post-pubertal uncomplicated chlamydia	M	1575	6654	13507
	F	4789	11766	16677
Herpes simplex first attack	M	381	2111	5924
	F	1244	3677	6622
Wart virus first attack	M	2753	13477	26372
	F	6517	15700	23145

Table 7.5 New cases of sexually transmitted diseases seen at genitourinary clinics by age, 1990

(ii) It could lead to a decrease in the stability of relationships by emphasising 'freedom' at the expense of 'responsibility'.

This could lead to the:
• undermining of the responsibilities of parenthood.
• breakdown of the family.

All of these phenomena are evident in society in Britain today. The reasons for their existence are undoubtedly complex and uncertain. What is certain is that they cannot be ignored. In 1989 there were 8342 recorded conceptions in the 13-15 age group, 15176 in 16 year olds and 32591 in 18 year olds in England and Wales.

◼ ABORTION

Abortion is difficult to define because the words used tend to betray the definer's viewpoint. Consider a definition: 'the miscarriage of the product of conception before the fetus (child) is viable, i.e. capable of a separate existence'.

Q 7. Does everyone in your group accept this definition. If not can you agree on another?

The two most common methods of abortion are suction and prostaglandin abortion. The first is used up to the twelfth week of pregnancy. Under general anaesthetic the cervix is gently stretched and the contents of the uterus are removed by suction. Beyond the twelfth week of pregnancy a change to the first method is needed as the cervix has to stretch more. This is done by passing a fluid containing hormones called prostaglandins into the uterus. The prostaglandins make the cervix open as the uterus contracts and this results in a miscarriage. A short operation under general anaesthetic usually follows to make sure the uterus is completely empty. Such simple, clinical descriptions should not be taken to imply that an abortion is an easy option. That is far from the truth for reasons which you may wish to discuss.

The history of abortion is probably as long as the history of pregnancy. There have been times when it was used as a form of population control but for most of history it has been carried out 'unofficially' and surrounded by controversy. In some countries though, it is widely used.

Abortion takes place in Britain against the background of an Act of Parliament which, since 1967, has defined the situations in which abortion can be carried out legally. Abortion is, however, still a crime under the Offences against the Person Act, 1861. The Abortion Act of 1967 has simply created exceptions to that rule: it has not allowed abortion on demand.

Q 8. Certificates, signed by two fully registered medical practitioners who form the opinion in good faith that a pregnancy should not be allowed to continue, permit an abortion. What possible reasons for such an opinion are recognised by the Abortion Act?

9. What circumstances do you think might provide grounds for abortion?

10. Does the 'father-to-be' have a right to veto a request for an abortion?

Since 1967 opponents of the Abortion Act have sought to remove it from the statute books or, at least, to amend it. The most recent attempt was Liberal MP David Alton's Abortion (Amendment) Bill. It proposed a reduction of the time limit for legal abortions from 28 to 18 weeks into pregnancy. There are a number of arguments on either side (see Table 7.6). In the event the bill resulted in a reduction of the time limit to 24 weeks.

The 1967 Act was designed to try to reduce the growing number of 'back-street' abortions and in this it was successful. Critics, however, will point to the annually increasing number of abortions being carried out. The Act does not resolve the moral issue as to whether the growing fetus is a 'human life' and whether even a therapeutic abortion is therefore a form of homicide.

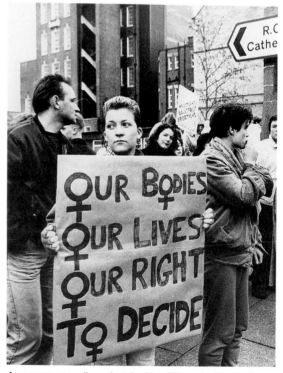

A protestor at a rally against the Alton Bill on abortion, 1988

	FOR	AGAINST
1	Human life is sacred. It begins at conception and by 18 weeks the baby is a fully-formed, unique human being with all its major organs functioning, apart from its lungs. The Society for the Protection of Unborn Children says: 'It is responsive to light, warmth, touch, sound and pain'.	Abortion is the lesser of two evils. The rights of the child have to be weighed against the rights of the mother. In the two years before the Abortion Act was passed in 1967, 98 women died from back-street abortions. In 1982 - 84 (the latest figures available) none did.
2	Late abortions are particularly repugnant. They involve greater trauma for the mother and pain for the fetus. They are appalling for medical staff, who hate carrying them out.	Late abortions should be reduced by preventing administrative delays, rather than by law. A fifth of women seeking abortion after 20 weeks have approached their doctor before the twelfth week.
3	The vast majority of late abortions are not done for reasons of fetal handicap (only **7.8** per cent in 1986), but for social reasons. In any case, handicapped children in the womb should be accorded the same rights as any other children.	Many late abortions are done on women in particularly vulnerable groups, such as the young or socially deprived. More than 640 were carried out for fetal handicap and these mothers should not be forced to continue their pregnancy.
4	New methods of early diagnosis make late abortion for fetal abnormality no longer necessary. A new technique, known as chorionic villus sampling (CVS), whereby a small piece of the mother's placenta is removed and analysed, can tell a mother at 10 weeks of pregnancy whether she is expecting a handicapped child.	A new method of early diagnosis, known as chorionic villus sampling, can detect only 20 per cent of fetal abnormalities. It cannot detect spina bifida, for example, a condition which can only be reliably diagnosed by amniocentesis or ultrasound scanning, the results of which are not available until after 18 weeks.
5	Almost half the abortions (45 per cent) carried out after 18 weeks are carried out on foreign women at private clinics for profit. Much of the opposition to the Bill come from doctors who are worried about losing their income.	Many late abortions are carried out on foreign women, mostly from Ireland, where abortion is illegal, or Spain, where it is very difficult. It is carried out in the private sector because the NHS gives priority to British residents.
6	Britain has much more liberal abortion laws than any other country in the Western world. No other country allows abortion as late as we do. The average abroad is 12-14 weeks of pregnancy.	Britain does not have the most liberal law in Europe. Our abortion rates per thousand women in 1984 were lower than in many other countries: 12.2 in the UK compared to 27.4 in the USA, 19.1 in Italy, 18.4 in Denmark and 15.2 in France.

Table 7.6 The arguments over the Alton Abortion Bill

■ SEXUALLY TRANSMITTED DISEASE (STD)

Diseases spread by contagion (direct contact) as in sexual contact were known as venereal diseases. The more usual term now is sexually transmitted disease (STD).

There is a danger that the existence of STD could become synonymous with AIDS (Acquired Immune Deficiency Syndrome). This is not to underestimate the importance of AIDS but to highlight the existence of at least three other sexualy transmitted diseases which should not be forgotten. Some idea of the number of patients with an STD is shown in Table 7.5 on page 85. There are, however, good reasons for focusing attention on AIDS.

Q 11. What makes AIDS so important?

In discussing this question with your group, you probably talked about personal implications of the question. However there are six main global, biological reasons for AIDS being important.

The first reason is that AIDS is a new infectious disease. A new disease is a rare phenomenon. Its novelty means that it comes upon a human population whose immune system has no experience of the disease agent. The implications of such an event were appreciated and exploited in the decimation of North American Indians by smallpox in the last century and of South American tribes more recently. Today we see the effects of a pathogen new to the entire human species. However, the species has a greater understanding of what it is up against and has some means of responding to it. AIDS seemed to make its appearance in 1980 in the United States, Africa and Europe simultaneously. Since then it has been possible to identify earlier cases in the late 1960s and 1970s and to trace its possible origin to Africa and to a mutated virus of the green monkey.

The second reason is that AIDS is caused by a virus. This means that it is difficult to detect and that it cannot be treated with antibiotics.

Q 12. Why can viruses not be attacked with antibiotics?

Despite the description of the syndrome between 1980 and 1981 and resources in laboratories all over the world devoted to the search for it, the cause of AIDS, i.e. the Human Immunedeficiency Virus (HIV) was not identified until April 1983. Furthermore, up to the present day there is no test for the virus itself. The test that is available is for antibodies to HIV. A person who is tested HIV positive is infected with HIV but does not necessarily have AIDS. This is because it may take several years after infection before the symptoms of AIDS develop. In some studies the *average* 'incubation' period was found to be eight years. Many people stay completely well whilst others develop minor illnesses without the total breakdown of the immune system. The minor symptoms are referred to as AIDS related complex (ARC). No one knows what proportion of HIV positive people will go on to develop AIDS. Some researchers believe all may do so eventually.

This uncertainty is the third reason for the importance of AIDS. It makes it difficult to know the true extent of the problem. Even current figures for full-blown AIDS are thought to be underestimates. By June 1992 British Government figures showed 6106 reported cases of AIDS. At the same time, nearly 17 000 people in Britain were recorded as HIV positive. Some idea of the age distribution of reported cases of AIDS in Britain during that time is shown in Figs.7.3(a) and 7.3(b).

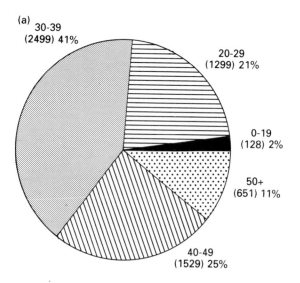

Figure 7.3 (a) Age distribution of AIDS reports; UK cumulative total to June 1992. (The total number of reports, where the age is known, is 6106.) The figures show the age group involved, e.g. 30-39, the number of people affected in that age group, e.g. (2499) and finally the percentage of the total, e.g. 41%.

(b)

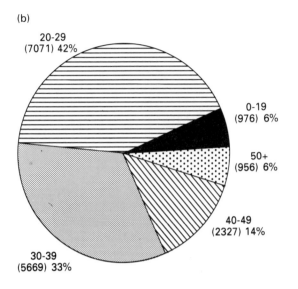

20-29
(7071) 42%

0-19
(976) 6%

50+
(956) 6%

40-49
(2327) 14%

30-39
(5669) 33%

Figure 7.3 (b) Age distribution of HIV reports; UK comulative total to June 1992. (The total number of reports, where the age is known, is 16 999.)

In 1989 the World Health Organisation estimated that between five and ten million people in the world were infected with HIV and that within the next five years there would be at least one million new cases of AIDS.

The fourth reason for the importance of AIDS relates to the way in which it is transmitted. The virus is present in the body fluids of an infected person but only in large enough quantities to be infectious in blood, semen and vaginal fluid (and possibly breast milk). It can therefore only be transmitted in three main ways:

• by sexual intercourse (heterosexual or homosexual).

• by contact with infected blood (e.g. through sharing needles to inject drugs).

• during pregnancy or childbirth from an infected mother to her child (and possibly by breast-feeding after birth).

Normal everyday contact with a person who has AIDS or who is HIV positive will not pass on the virus. The particular pattern of spread now varies with local factors. Promiscuity coupled with the absence of symptoms from many infectious individuals makes the prevention of the spread of the virus difficult to achieve. More than this, however, it raises certain personal, social and

ethical issues which you may like to discuss:

• Compensation for haemophiliacs who were accidentally infected with contaminated Factor VIII or transfused blood used in their treatment before all blood products were tested for HIV antibodies.

• The moral dilemma of prospective parenthood for an HIV positive woman.

• The risk of isolation of people with AIDS or HIV through prejudice or ignorance about the transmission of the virus.

• The problem of getting the message over to a variety of target groups that we need to stop the spread of HIV, and of influencing people to practice safer sex and use a condom during intercourse.

The fifth reason for the importance of AIDS is the means by which HIV attacks the body. As its name suggests, HIV affects certain cells of the immune system whose job is to fight off infection. As a result the key white blood cells of the immune system (called T-cells) decline in number until virtually none remain. Without them a number of usually harmless infections and some rare cancers can become killers. Because it undermines the immune system the most common symptoms of HIV infection are similar to those that might be associated with a variety of other conditions such as flu, the common cold or even certain forms of stress. These are not however a clear guide for self-diagnosis and a person who might be at risk should therefore seek medical advice.

The sixth reason for a heightened awareness of AIDS is the current state of the fight against it. Although there is as yet no cure for AIDS nor a vaccine against it, research is continuing. The drug Zidovudine (formerly known as AZT) which initially reduced the death rate in people with AIDS proved to have toxic side-effects. It is now undergoing further trials. Some scientists believe that the unusual complicated life cycle of the virus offers greater opportunities for the discovery of a drug capable of inhibiting one of its stages. A vaccine is at present undergoing field trials but it is believed that, unlike most vaccines which help the body to generate its own immune response, a HIV vaccine must also stimulate the production of immune cells which can kill cells infected with HIV. This reflects the theory that HIV antibodies (the basis of the 'test' for AIDS) fail to limit the infection. This may be because the virus is inside the host cells or because infected cells can migrate and

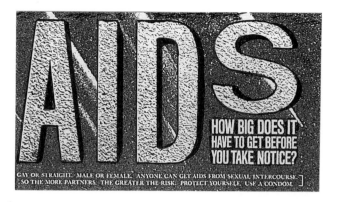

AIDS

HOW BIG DOES IT HAVE TO GET BEFORE YOU TAKE NOTICE?

GAY OR STRAIGHT. MALE OR FEMALE. ANYONE CAN GET AIDS FROM SEXUAL INTERCOURSE - SO THE MORE PARTNERS, THE GREATER THE RISK. PROTECT YOURSELF. USE A CONDOM.

become localised in parts of the body like the brain, where they escape the immune system.

The case of AIDS has, however, provided a stimulus for a great deal of valuable research not the least of which is into the nature of human sexual behaviour - a subject which is still something of a taboo. It has also led to a growing awareness that AIDS is something that potentially affects us all - a necessary realisation if the threat it poses is to be overcome.

■ SEXUAL ORIENTATION

Homosexuality (the erotic love of an individual for another of the same sex) has existed throughout history and has been viewed in different ways at different times and in different cultures.

There is evidence that virtually all animals from insects to large mammals display homosexual behaviour but it is unusual for sexual behaviour to be exclusively homosexual. In human society there is a spectrum of sexual behaviour patterns from exclusively heterosexual through bisexual to exclusively homosexual. Homosexual men are known as gay men and homosexual women are known as lesbians. The 1948 Kinsey report on sexual behaviour of the American male first defined this spectrum and concluded that four per cent of American men were exclusively homosexual. If we view sexual behaviour to be primarily procreative, i.e. concerned with reproduction, then a pattern of exclusively homosexual behaviour, as observed in a significant proportion of men and women, would be considered unusual. A failure to appreciate the difference between 'unusual' and 'unnatural' has been responsible for a great deal of the distress suffered by homosexuals up to the present day.

It is not surprising that the search for a cause of an unusual behaviour pattern should be mistrusted by homosexuals and lead to a lack of co-operation. The attitudes of society have led to fears that such a search is the first step towards looking for a 'cure'. The implication that homosexuality is an illness is understandably rejected by the homosexual community. In Britain, in 1967, the Government removed penalties for homosexual acts which take place in private between consenting adult men over the age of 21. As a result some research has been possible into the causes. The outcome of this research has been to provide a greater understanding, a number of theories, but no conclusions. Underlying all of the theories is a general acceptance of the idea that every person has characteristics of both sexes. The idea was put forward by Carl Jung, one of the 'fathers' of psychoanalysis. It reflects the Kinsey spectrum of sexual behaviour and of the traditional male and female characteristics, and the fact that oestrogen and testosterone are both produced by both sexes. To Jung, the nature of the individual represented the extent to which the aspect opposite to their genetic determinants is expressed or suppressed.

Q 13. What is your reaction to requests:
a) from homosexual couples who want to adopt children?
b) from lesbians who want to be artificially impregnated?

14. Female homosexuality has never attracted the same social stigma as male homosexuality nor has it been a criminal offence in Britain. What reasons can you suggest for this difference in attitude?

■ SEXUAL EQUALITY

Much has been written on this subject especially since the sexual revolution of the 1960s. Two major questions are particularly important in this context.

 15. What are the differences between the sexes?

16. What is the present status of women in society in Britain?

The Power Game

Men and women look and seem different; experts disagree as to whether they *are* immutably different. What nobody argues about is the fact that their lives are different. And - at the end of a century of feminist endeavour - they are not equal. Men and women in Britain are nowhere near equality yet.

Women do not have equality with men at work; at home; in the classroom; in marriage; on the streets; in the professions. Women have less money, power, prestige, status and say than men. (Their earnings were 66 per cent of men's last year; of people earning £500 a week or more, only six per cent were women.)

There are still infinitely fewer women than men who are successful financiers, politicians, philosophers, conductors, chefs, jockeys, pilots, editors, scientists or train-drivers; or who are eminent enough at anything to merit an entry in 'Who's Who'. Women compose almost half the country's workforce but only ten per cent of its senior civil servants, two per cent of its surgeons, three per cent of its judges, eight per cent of its chartered accountants.

It is a sorry picture. Biological determinists say it's all because women aren't designed to fight for their survival like men. Most women put the blame on their inheritance of two millennia of patriarchy.

THE GREAT DIVIDE

After almost two decades of women's liberation, are the sexes any closer in equality or compatability? Or are men still warriors and hunters, aggressive, promiscuous and dominant; chiefly interested in work, weapons and territory, and better than women at mathematics and chess? Are women, meanwhile, complementarily passive, submissive and monogamous, born to make homes and rear children, happiest when nesting, nurturing and 'relating', and better than men with words?

Professor Jeffrey Gray of the Institute of Psychiatry in London writes 'I am in no way a male chauvinist,' he says. 'One can believe in biological sex differences and in the equality of treatment for the sexes. But I would say that it is quite impossible to find any

part of the human anatomy - not only the genitals - that is not constructed differently in men and women. There are differences in brain functioning; in the hormonal and endocrine systems; in sensory capacities; in the amount and distribution of fat on the body - even in the way we throw things or play as children. And the same is true of temperamental and intellectual characteristics. To try to suppress behaviours that come out of them - like the way little boys play with guns - is a bit like the Catholic Church trying to make more people celibate - not impossible, but difficult.'

'Nobody disputes that there are greater differences within the sexes than between them,' says Dr Geoff Sanders, a biologist-turned-

psychologist at the City University in London.

Women have about 15 per cent more fat and weaker muscles than men, and the average man runs faster than the average woman. Yet some women are thinner and stronger than some men. Some women can run faster than most men. There is less than a second's difference between the world 100 metres' records of men and women; and women are getting faster quicker than men - recent predictions based on empirical data show that women will be reaching records equal to men in the 1990. (though their fertility and menstruation, i.e. their femaleness, may suffer in the process).

■ FERTILITY CONTROL

Progress in contraception has led to an increased understanding of infertility. Methods of treatment which have allowed otherwise infertile couples to become parents are now available. In some cases, however, the research and development involved has given rise to further controversy. To be successful the method of treatment must be chosen to match the problem. A low sperm count can be treated by collecting semen, concentrating the sperm and introducing the sperm into the woman's body artificially. This is called artificial insemination. Failure to ovulate can be overcome by hormone treatment to trigger the ripening process in the ovary. In its early days this treatment led to a number of celebrated multiple births. It has since continued with greater (if less spectacular) success.

Aspects of these techniques have been exploited more recently to achieve *in vitro* fertilisation (IVF) (literally meaning 'fertilisation in glass'). The first convincing demonstration of IVF with a human sperm and egg was reported in 1969. Since then it has been combined with embryo transfer (ET) by which an embryo at an early stage is placed into the uterus of the mother. The first such 'test-tube baby', Louise Brown, was born in 1978 and in the ten years after that over 4000 babies were born with the help of this treatment. Although this represents a significant number of new parents among couples who would otherwise be infertile, the success rate of this treatment is still only 1 in 10. IVF is of particular importance that it addresses a cause of infertility in the woman, namely a blockage or other conditions in the oviduct which inhibit fertilisation.

A further cause of infertility with an even more controversial treatment is failure of implantation. In recent years 'surrogate pregnancy' has been used to overcome this problem. In such cases a woman volunteers or contracts to carry the embryo or fetus and give birth to the child of a woman whose uterus rejects implantation or miscarries. In some cases the surrogate mother also donates the egg, so complicating the legal situation even further on the question of 'whose baby is it, anyway?'

These issues of human and social biology focus our attention on questions about the nature and

SURROGATE PREGNANCY

Earlier this year there was an energetic campaign by a number of scientists to secure the passing of the Embryo Bill, which would allow experiments on embryos up to 14 days old. Many assurances were given about the responsibility of scientists, and the unlikelihood of their abusing their powers for genetic experiments.

It is interesting to see that one of the pioneers of embryology and test-tube births, Professor Robert Edwards, is now involved with a private clinic to provide 'surrogate mothers' to bear the children of couples who are unable to have them in the normal way. Dr Edwards and his colleagues at Bourn Hall Clinic, near Cambridge, are keen to stress their concern with ethical issues. It is, of course, illegal to make money out of surrogacy. But couples will have to pay £2,500 for a child, which will apparently cover the mother's expenses and 'compensate her for loss of earnings'.

As far as genetics is concerned, this is the beginning of our Brave New World. Professor Edwards has already predicted that the techniques which he has pioneered could be used in the future by busy career women who do not wish to give birth themselves.

Quite apart from any ethical considerations, such experiments ought to be made illegal because of the disputes over parenthood that will arise inevitably. But Parliament has swallowed hook, line and sinker the scientists' clever propaganda that nothing whatever should stand in the way of a couple who want to have a child.

quality of life, i.e. on questions about ethics. In connection with human reproduction it comes down to questions such as, 'Is abortion ever justified?', 'Should research on human embryos be allowed?', 'Should prospective parents have the right to choose or manipulate the genetic characteristics of their baby?', 'Should human cloning be allowed?' The answers we find to such questions will reflect much about the values held by our society.

Many writers have speculated that it is a uniquely human capacity to have an awareness that we are going to die. Attitudes to these 'intimations of mortality' may influence many aspects of our lives. Some may regard sexual reproduction as a partial means of 'genetic' immortality. Cloning may hold the prospect of individual genetic immortality. Most of the world's major religions offer the hope of immortality in some form. Cultural evolution offers yet another means of a form of 'immortality' through the writing and other artefacts that people leave to society. However, this is not a genetic form of immortality.

Current biological research points towards the death of the individual as being inevitable. Individual life expectancy can be prolonged but only within the pre-programmed average span of 85 years. Perhaps genetic engineering will change this situation in the future. The central practical issue, however, is likely to remain coming to terms with the ageing and death of the body from natural cau*ses*. Leaving aside the tragedies of untimely death and death due to unnatural causes, different communities have various ways of coping with death.

In Chapter 4 we discussed some recent advances in our understanding of ageing. It appears that the increase in life expectancy achieved in recent years is not associated with any increase in the maximum life span. This means that the major causes of death must be ageing or age-related diseases. These include cardiac and circulatory diseases, strokes, cancer, arthritis, diabetes, renal failure and Alzheimer's disease. Research into each of these has separate funding, mostly by charitable foundations, and much progress has been made. In the West a large proportion of health care budgets is now assigned to providing care for the elderly and the population pyramids in Chapter 3 indicate the growing proportion of the population in the Western world that is elderly.

The treatments of many age-related diseases are expensive and it is an unfortunate fact that the prevention or cure of one age-related disease is often followed by the onset of another. The most likely explanation for this deterioration is the accumulation of basic defects in cells and their biochemistry in all parts of the body.

 17. Would it be better to spend money on research into the process of ageing itself rather than into individual age-related diseases?

18. In the long term can we justify the money spent on life-support systems, in particular, when the quality of life that is supported is very poor?

There are two aspects of the quality of life of the

elderly which you might like to discuss. The first concerns the provision made by society for those who have 'retired'.

The second aspect concerns health. As people live longer the incidence of age-related diseases increases. It could be that research into ageing can prolong healthy old age until an individual is close to death.

 19. In what ways do we undervalue the elderly in our society?

20. How could we provide opportunities for the elderly to enjoy a better quality of life?

There are, however, situations in which the dignity of a human being is undermined by age-related disease. What is to be done then? You will have read or heard of cases of this kind.

Euthanasia is the name given to the bringing about of a person's death at his or her own request in order to save him or her from unnecessary suffering. At present it is illegal in Britain. What do you think?

Why I helped my mother to die

On the night of 16 March 1989, Phillipa Monaghan gave her mother - at her request - a large quantity of sleeping pills, holding her hand as she passed away. Months of suffering came to an end.

It all started in 1986, when doctors told her mother, 48-year-old Sylvia Williams, that she was suffering from motor neurone disease, which slowly destroys the nervous system and for which there is no cure. By early 1989, Mrs Williams was almost completely paralysed. Her voice was going and her breathing was affected. But her brain was not and she asked Phillipa and her sisters to help her take her own life.

Shortly afterwards she [Phillipa] went to her local police station and confessed. Four months later she was tried, convicted of attempted murder and placed on probation for two years.

The judge concluded: 'I think you have suffered enough. You are obviously a caring and loving person and you did what you did because you couldn't bear to see your mother suffer. She wanted to die and brought great emotional pressure to bear on you to help her terminate her own life. It is not possible to say whether what you did caused the final result. The law cannot condone what you did. It was unlawful but I can show you mercy.'

DRUGS AND SOCIETY

Two extracts from popular magazines during one month of 1990 sought to give help and advice about drugs.

TRANQUILLISERS

Tranquillisers have been in use now for nearly thirty years. The 'major' ones, prescribed long term for serious mental illness such as schizophrenia, have undoubtedly transformed life for millions of sufferers, enabling them to enjoy - or at least to cope with - their everyday lives. The so-called 'minor' tranquillisers are different. Hailed at first as the answer to any emotional distress or sleep difficulties, it now seems they can cause more problems than they solve.

These minor tranquillisers all come from the group known chemically as benzodiazepines and there is no significant difference between those prescribed for anxiety and those prescribed for sleep problems. They can also act as a powerful muscle relaxant and produce drowsiness - useful for minor operations. The most common include Valium, Librium, Ativan, Tranxene, Serenid, Mogadon, Noctamid and Normison.

Every year one in seven adults takes tranquillisers at some time and about a quarter of a million have been taking them for more than five years. Prescribed for a short while (no longer than four weeks is usually recommended) to help you over a particularly distressing time in your life, they can be very useful, but studies have shown that dependency can develop soon after this.

Anxiety, like pain, is a healthy warning to us that something is wrong in our lives - worries about relationships, money or work, for example. Tranquillisers won't solve the underlying problem: they will only temporarily relieve some of the symptoms that anxiety can produce, like a racing heart, sleeplessness and feelings of panic, dizziness and irritability.

Problems can occur when a person comes to rely on the calming effect of tranquillisers after the original distressing event is well past. Emotions become dulled, concentration is difficult, and work and relationships may suffer. Without the tranquillisers, *withdrawal symptoms* may be similar to, or worse than the symptoms those for which the drugs were initially prescribed. The sufferer needs more tranquillisers to cope with these symptoms - and vicious a circle develops.

Woman's Weekly 30 January 1990

Addiction: Come off drugs safely

The terms *'addiction'* and '**withdrawal**' conjure up pictures of hypodermic syringes and junkies. It seems totally removed from tranquillisers - pills prescribed by the doctor. But more and more women are now discovering the nightmare of withdrawal symptoms from tranquilliser addiction. Health authorities are reporting a dramatic rise in the number of 'tranquilliser addicts' admitted to hospital as doctors try to wean them off pills. A letter from a consultant psychiatrist in *The Lancet* medical journal highlights concern that GPs are taking patients off the drugs too abruptly. The doctors are worried that they could face legal action if they don't wean patients off the drugs as quickly as possible, the psychiatrist claims. More than 1,500 people have applied for legal aid for tranquilliser addiction claims.

Woman 15 January 1990

Q 1. What pictures do the words drug, addiction and withdrawal, conjure up for you? Discuss your ideas with your colleagues before you look up any definitions.

2. Why does the article from *Woman* refer to 'more and more women'? Twice as many women as men take tranquillisers, and women continue taking these drugs for longer. Why should this be so?

3. There is concern that GPs are taking patients off tranquillisers too abruptly. Should there be concern that doctors may put patients on to these drugs too readily?

4. Do you think it is fair that doctors may face legal action in a case of tranquilliser addiction, or were they only doing their job in continuing to prescribe tranquillisers?

Figure 8.1

withdrawal symptoms if a person's body has become adapted to the presence of a particular drug, and then the person stops taking it, the body reacts to its absence. The symptoms, severity and duration of withdrawal effects vary with different drugs and with different people

addiction if a person's dependence on a drug detrimentally affects his of her whole life style and relationships in society, the person is considered to be addicted. It is a social definition rather than a medical one, i.e. it reflects society's attitute to the drug-dependent person

■ DRUG LAWS

The Misuse of Drugs Act classifies certain drugs into three classes with different penalties for offences involving drugs of each class. Class A drugs incur the highest penalties, Class C the lowest.

Except in cases of medical prescription or other authorisation, it is an offence to possess, produce, supply or offer to supply illegal drugs. It is an offence to allow your premises to be used for the use, production or supply of illegal drugs.

Those drugs which are not controlled by the Misuse of Drugs Act may have limitations on their supply through the Medicines Act, or have special legislation relating to them, as in the case of alcohol and cigarettes. Some drug sources, e.g. coffee, glue solvents, and magic mushrooms have few or no legal restrictions on their supply and use.

■ WHAT ARE DRUGS?

The word 'drug' is used in many contexts, mostly with emotive overtones. A drug is a substance taken into the body, which does not provide energy or growth material, but which can affect the metabolism of the body. Vitamins and mineral compounds, taken as supplements to the normal diet may be considered as drugs. Hormones, similar to those produced naturally in the body, may be administered as drugs for therapeutic, contraceptive, fertility enhancing or performance enhancing purposes.

Medicines which disrupt the metabolism of our bodies' parasites, with minimal effect on the human metabolism, are used as drugs to treat diseases caused by pathogen organisms. Some of these medicinal drugs are derived from 'natural' sources, such as plants, while others are chemically synthesised. Many medicinal drugs act by disturbing the metabolism of a particular tissue or organ or by interfering with a particular chemical process, thus readjusting the body to 'normal'.

Most drugs have some effect on the mind, but those which bring noticeable psychological changes, or modify mental activity in human beings, are called psychotropic drugs. Most human societies use, or have used, naturally occurring psychotropic substances, e.g. alcohol, tobacco, coffee, marijuana, peyote, amanita and opium, for recreational purposes and ritual, as well as for therapeutic purposes. Synthetic compounds such as heroin, amphetamines, barbiturates and LSD are newer psychotropic drugs.

■ Types of drugs

Stimulants speed up the activity of the brain and other organs. They wake people up and make them more alert and active. They act as anti-depressant drugs.

Depressants slow the activity of the brain. They calm people down and cause sleep. They can be relaxants, tranquillisers or sedatives.

Hallucinogens or *psychedelic* drugs affect the perceptions. They allow people to perceive everyday things more vividly or to perceive non-existent things (hallucinations) and confuse them with reality.

Q 5. Can you think of an example of a hallucinogenic or psychodelic drug?

■ DEPENDENCE

If a person takes a drug regularly, he or she may get to a stage of compulsion to continue taking the drug. This compulsion may be psychological dependence, in that the person needs the stimulation, pleasure, or desire to obliterate reality that the drug provides them. Physical dependence is a compulsion to continue taking the drug to which the body has adapted, in order to avoid the physical discomfort of withdrawal.

■ DRUGS IN SOCIETY

The attitude of society to certain drugs varies in different cultures and at different times. In seventeenth century England, drinking coffee was thought rather risqué. In Victorian times, however, opium, in the form of pills or as the alcoholic solution called laudanum, was available to anyone from a grocer's shop. The Pharmacy Act of 1868 limited the sale of opium to chemists' shops, but did not restrict the quantities supplied nor to whom. It was commonly used by a wide range of people to dull their pain or misery.

Cocaine and cannabis were similarly available in the late nineteenth century, though they were less widely used by the general public. In contemporary Britain the psychotropic drugs alcohol, nicotine and caffeine are socially acceptable. Their use is informally controlled by the habits of various subcultures and by licensing and sales restrictions for alcohol and nicotine.

The terms drug abuse and drug misuse suggest that the drug taking is a harmful use of the drug or a socially unacceptable use of the drug, respectively. These are subjective and emotive terms, not precisely linked with any medical or legal definitions. Non-medical drug use has an obvious and less subjective meaning.

Alcohol

'Whether we drink heavily, moderately, or are totally abstinent, we all possess a host of common-sense understandings concerning the effects of alcohol on our body. The bits and pieces of evidence upon which these shared understandings are based come to us from a wide variety of sources - parents, peers, schools, books, magazines, radio and television programmes, movies, and of course, our own everyday experiences.'

The writers of the above comment, MacAndrew and Edgerton, believe that the perceptions and behaviour associated with drinking and drunkenness are not just due to the chemical effects of ethanol on the nervous system - they depend on the norms and values associated with alcohol which are culturally and socially defined.

Many people enjoy a glass of beer, wine or spirits in a social setting, as the tranquillising effect of alcohol helps them to relax and feel at ease with other people. Alcohol is probably not harmful, and indeed may be beneficial, as long as a person limits his or her weekly intake to the recommended levels of 21 units for a man or 14 units for a woman (see Fig.8.2). However, a British Government report in 1989 estimated that 27 per cent of men and 15 per cent of women were drinking above sensible limits. Alcohol is the most common cause of serious drug dependence in Britain, with up to 5 per cent of the population being affected. Figure 8.3 shows the steady rise in alcohol consumption, deaths and affordability.

1 unit of alcohol is equal to:

1/2 pint of beer of lager

or 1 glass of wine

or 1 measure of spirits

Safe drinking levels for adults

21 units per week   14 units per week

Figure 8.2 Units of alcohol chart

Alcohol depresses the brain function and is *anxiolytic* (anxiety-dissolving). People often start drinking heavily to escape their worries but the body becomes *tolerant* to the tranquillising effect; this leads to a progressive increase in the amount drunk in order to obtain the tranquillising effect. Not every heavy drinker is an alcoholic, dependent on alcohol and unable to control his or her habit. The causes of alcoholism are not fully understood; emotional deprivation and genetic factors controlling biochemical reactions may be predisposing conditions. The compulsion to become intoxicated leads to physical damage to the stomach, liver, pancreas, heart, brain and bone marrow. Death may result from the failure of one of these organs, but it is common for alcoholics to die through accidents, suicide or inhalation of vomit whilst drunk. Even if alcoholic addiction is not fatal it can be socially disruptive as the person cannot manage their family life and their work.

Heavy drinkers who escape becoming addicted to alcohol are still susceptible to the toxic effects of the drug such as cirrhosis of the liver and various forms of cancer.

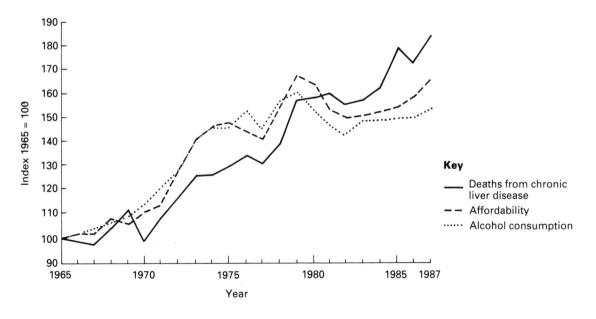

Figure 8.3 Alcohol consumption, deaths and affordability. (Affordability = $\frac{\text{disposable income}}{\text{price of alcohol}}$)

A person under the influence of alcohol may be violent causing damage to property, other people and herself or himself. The lager lout issue may be exaggerated but it has helped to focus attention on the prevalence of alcohol abuse amongst young people. At worst, the drunken person may cause death to herself or himself, a friend, a family member and others.

Although the number of deaths and alcohol-related road accidents was more than halved between 1979 and 1991, drunken drivers are still responsible for about 800 deaths a year in Britain. One in six road deaths is drink-related. The most common cause of death among the under twenty five age group is road accidents, many of which are drink related.

Research and experience show that none of the varied medical treatments in use have had much influence on the course of alcohol dependence, nor can the physical complications of prolonged heavy drinking be cured. Professor Kendell of Edinburgh University, speaking about this problem in 1989, said that 'the physician's role in treatment should be focused mainly on brief simple interventions designed to persuade heavy drinkers to reduce their consumption at an early stage and to teach them strategies for doing so'. He suggested that the treatment of established dependence is more effectively dealt with by psychologists, social workers and self-help groups like Alcoholics Anonymous.

■ 'RESPECTABLE' ADDICTS

Drug misuse and dependence is usually thought to be associated with the youth subculture, petty crime and evil pushers who exploit the addicts' need.

Recently another group of addicts has been featured in the medical and popular press, such as in the articles at the beginning of this chapter. These are people suffering from *iatrogenic* (caused by doctors) dependence on tranquillisers. These anxiolytic drugs are only available on prescription from a medical practitioner but they are subject to minimal regulations, unlike 'controlled drugs'. The people who are hooked on to such drugs are mostly 'respectable' middle-aged women who have relied on their doctors to help them deal with their anxiety states. There is evidence that a high proportion of women consulting their doctors

with headache symptoms are treated with tranquillisers, whereas a similar proportion of male headache sufferers are referred for hospital examination. The British National Formulary, a list of medical drugs, reminds the prescriber that he or she has three main responsibilities in prescribing drugs likely to cause dependence or misuse. The first is to avoid creating dependence by introducing drugs to patients without sufficient reason, as there has been uninhibited prescribing resulting in a very large number of patients taking tablets which do them neither much good nor much harm, but which they cannot easily give up. The second responsibility is to see that the patient does not gradually increase the dose of a drug, given for good medical reasons, to the point where dependence becomes more likely. The third responsibility is to avoid the drug being used as an unwitting source for supply to addicts.

Many doctors have not recognised the dependence of their patients on tranquillisers but now that the problem is well known, patients have become aware of their own addiction. Self-help groups have been formed to provide support for fellow sufferers and there is pressure on doctors to help patients come off the drugs gradually and safely.

Q 5. Is anxiety really a psychological illness? Many people go to their doctors with anxiety symptoms because they have nobody else in whom they can confide their problems. Should society provide counselling services for people with problems which are not medical in origin? What other forms of support and treatment should be available for people suffering anxiety?

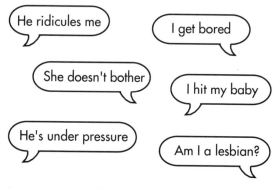

Anxious cries for help appear in many 'Agony Aunt' columns in magazines. Who should help manage anxiety? Are drugs the solution?

Figure 8.4 Health (mis)information

■ HEALTH INFORMATION OR MISINFORMATION

Look at the statements in Fig.8.4 and decide whether they are true or false.

You may say that these statements are far too simple, as they suggest simple cause and effect relationships between one factor and a health problem. Even if there were some connection between the variables, we know that they do not hold true in every case. These statements are obviously generalisations from large samples of people. Look at the statements again: true or false? Discuss your answers with your colleagues.

Q 6. How do you know the answers?

7. How do the scientists know?

8. How does the public get to know?

■ EPIDEMIOLOGY

Etiology (or aetiology) is the study of the causes of diseases. How do scientists set about finding the causes of diseases or disabilities? An important approach is through *epidemiology*. Epidemiology is the study of patterns of health and disease in human populations, based on the methods of social and statistical sciences as well as on medical diagnoses. It includes the study of the patterns of birth rates, death rates and the incidence of certain diseases in various groups within society.

Apart from identifying possible causative or conditioning factors for particular diseases, epidemiology provides information needed for planning health and social services.

The stimulus for embarking on a particular study is often the recognition by health workers of the widespread occurrence (an *epidemic*) of a particular disease. In the 1950s doctors noticed that over the previous 40 years there had been a

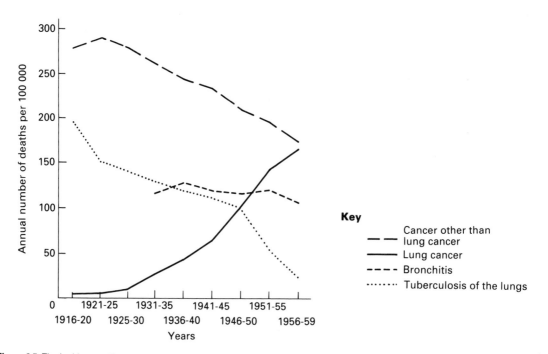

Figure 8.5 The incidence of lung cancer and other diseases in men aged 45-64 from 1916-59. The increasing death rate from lung cancer over this period is most striking. The decline in deaths from other forms of cancer has occurred chiefly in respect of cancer of the liver, tongue, oesophagus and rectum. The sharp decline in tuberculous mortality in the last decade is largely attributable to modern treatment. Bronchitis mortality rates before 1931 were much higher than subsequently, but, because of changes in the practice of death registration, the earlier figures are not comparable to subsequent ones and have been omitted. Since 1931 bronchitis death rates in middle-aged men have changed very little

large increase in the incidence of lung cancer, while other lung diseases and other cancers had decreased (Fig.8.5). The incidence of lung cancer had also increased much more for men than for women.

To account for this increase, scientists sought some causative agent to which human lungs, particularly men's, had been newly and increasingly exposed during the first half of the twentieth century. Cigarette smoke appeared to be a likely candidate.

▮ Research into the effects of smoking

Epidemiological research is often based on *retrospective* (looking back) surveys. A number of such studies were undertaken in many countries to investigate the hypothesis that lung cancer is associated with smoking. The investigators 'looked back' by asking questions about the smoking habits of large samples of patients suffering from lung cancer and large control groups of people

who did not have this disease.

Among the lung cancer patients there was a higher proportion of heavy smokers and a smaller proportion of light smokers or non-smokers than in the control groups.

The retrospective studies have been confirmed by *prospective* (looking forwards) studies in several countries. Such studies take longer because they consist of recording the habits and circumstances of sample groups over many years, then noting the subsequent illnesses and causes of death that these people suffer. In a twenty-year research programme, from 1951, Doll and Hill studied 35 000 doctors. The subjects were monitored by means of questionnaires on their smoking habits and other particulars. The population was from one profession so that wide variations in socio-economic class and other factors were limited. After allowing for variables of age, sex and home areas it was clear that lung cancer developed more frequently among the

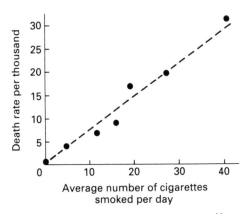

Figure 8.6 Death rate from lung cancer among men smoking different daily numbers of cigarettes at the start of a prospective study (1964)

cigarette-smoking group than amongst non-smokers. The data showed a qualitative relationship: there was a steady increase in numbers of deaths from lung cancer with increasing cigarette consumption, both in the numbers of cigarettes per day and the number of years that people had smoked (Fig.8.6).

They also showed that the lung cancer risk among those who have given up smoking for several years was less than among those who continue to smoke.

The evidence of this study influenced people to accept a causal relationship between cigarette smoking and lung cancer. Since then, several other diseases have been found to be caused or aggravated by smoking. They include bronchitis, emphysema, coronary heart disease, cancer of the throat and cancer of the bladder. Smoking during pregnancy has a deleterious effect on mother and fetus.

It is estimated that there are 100 000 smoking-related deaths a year in Britain, and two million world-wide. The direct treatment costs to the NHS alone are estimated at £500 million annually.

■ Tobacco

Tobacco contains the drug nicotine which is a stimulant. It enables smokers to maintain performance in tiring and monotonous situations. However, in some circumstances it has a tranquillising effect alleviating stress and anxiety. The effects are immediate but short-lived, hence the tendency to chain-smoke. Dependence is readily established; withdrawal symptoms include irritability and depression. The *carcinogenic*

components of tobacco smoke are tars and other irritants. Smoke also contains carbon monoxide which can pass from a mother who smokes to her unborn child, stunting its growth.

In recent years the dangers of passive smoking have been recognised. The non-smoking families and colleagues of smokers have been shown to suffer from smoking-related diseases. Public pressure has resulted in smoking-free zones in cinemas, theatres, restaurants, transport and other public places though some smokers regard this as an infringement of their right to indulge in their habit.

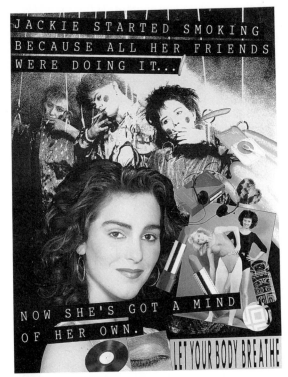

Q 9. Look back at the statements on page 99. Which of these could be investigated by:
a) a retrospective study?
b) a prospective study?

10. What are the advantages and disadvantages of each kind of study?

11. Sometimes epidemiologists can make use of natural experiments. These are situations when a population is subjected to possibly hazardous conditions because of a chance or accidental event. Can you think of any recent events which have provided such natural experiments?

■ Heroin

The myths about drugs suppose that all drug users are or will become like the stereotypical heroin junkie.

Heroin is one of the opiate drugs derived from the opium poppy. Opium contains morphine and codeine, both used as medical drugs. Heroin is a more potent, white power made from morphine. Heroin can be sniffed, smoked or injected. Contrary to popular opinion, heroin is not an instantly addictive drug and not all heroin users are addicts. Opiates induce a relaxed detachment from pain, desires and anxiety. They make people feel sleepy, warm and content. Different levels of use can be identified, from non-use, through experimentation with the initial offer, to occasional use on a recreational basis. This may lead to psychological and physical dependence and tolerance, involving compulsive use. Then the person has to obtain the drug just to stay feeling normal. The passage between these levels can be thought of as transition points; they are not inevitable transitions.

Heroin and similar opiates are Class A drugs. As with alcohol, many of the expectations about heroin use and its effects are culturally based. One of the myths is that people are introduced to hard drugs by professional 'pushers'. In reality, the initial offer of heroin occurs almost invariably within a friend-ship group. If people are to be encouraged to say 'No', they must be aware that it is more likely to be 'No' to a gift from a friend than 'No' to an evil stranger.

Another false stereotype is that of the horrors of 'cold turkey', the withdrawal symptoms of coming off the drug. These may have been exaggerated to try to deter people from experimenting with the drug. There is evidence that overemphasis of the pain of withdrawal discourages heroin users from trying to kick the habit, rather than discouraging others from starting. For most regular users, abstinence from heroin produces withdrawal symptoms similar to flu. Withdrawal causes the user's tolerance to fade, such that if a person then resumes his or her accustomed dose he or she may overdose his or her body and enter a coma and possibly die. The mythology of opiate use, including romantic associations with heroes of the rock world, tends to isolate users from the support of their families and from assistance in giving up the drug habit.

■ COMPLICATIONS OF DRUG USE

Many hard drug users are unable to give up their habit. Some addicts who can afford to live an otherwise healthy lifestyle, survive normally with little apparent impairment to their health. Many addicts are not known as such until they die as a direct or indirect result of their habits. However, some eventually conform to the stereotype of the down-and-out junkie. Many addicts become unable to maintain family and employment situations and live in squalid conditions, eating a poor diet. Their habit may become very expensive and they may turn to crime to support it. They may not have the facilities or the motivation to use clean equipment for injecting drugs. Intravenous drug users sharing needles are at risk from hepatitis B, HIV, tetanus and other infections. Some people take mixed drugs, either deliberately or inadvertently because drug traders dilute heroin with a cheaper barbiturate. Overdosage of a drug is common as a cause of death.

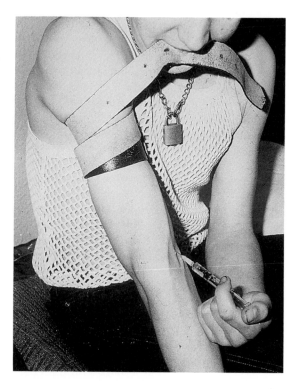

A heroin addict 'shooting up'. The strap tightened around his upper arm makes the veins swell up so that the injection is easier to perform

■ EFFECTS OF DRUGS

From the discussion of tranquillisers, alcohol, tobacco and heroin in this chapter, it can be seen that the word drugs is a term which covers many different substances. Responses to drugs differ between people, both as individual users and as members of society. The majority of people who use drugs come to no serious harm. But the effects of drugs are not just pharmacological; they are also due to social expectations and the environment in which they are taken. Some people take drugs to try to forget or to cope with problems. It is then difficult to dissociate the continued effects of those problems from the effects of the drugs.

There are serious direct risks from taking drugs in large or continued doses, in mixtures, or when in poor physical or psychological health. Not only alcohol but most other drugs impair motor control, reaction time, and the ability to maintain attention. They also weaken social and personal inhibitions. These effects contribute to the indirect risks of drug-taking, in connection with driving, operating machinery, concentrating on study or work, getting into unintentional aggressive or sexual situations, not to mention getting into trouble with the law.

People vary in their susceptibility to their dependence on drugs. Knowledge of the action of drugs does not protect against dependence; medical personnel have a higher rate of addiction than the general population, possibly because they have easier access to addictive drugs.

The following paragraphs below give outline information about the non-medical use of some other drugs.

■ Amphetamines

Amphetamines or pep pills (speed) are stimulant drugs. They are made for medical use but are also taken illegally. Some are Class C drugs, others Class B, and if prepared for injection they become Class A.

Amphetamines may be taken as pills by mouth or the powdered form may be injected, smoked or sniffed. They have a similar effect to adrenaline in the body. At first, the user feels more energetic, confident and cheerful, and so there is a risk of psychological but not physical dependence. Later effects include anxiety, irritability and tiredness. High dosage and long-term use can produce delirium, panic, hallucinations, paranoia and other mental and physical ill-effects.

■ Cocaine

Cocaine is a white powder derived from the leaves of the South American coca plant. (Note: This is not the cocoa plant from which chocolate is manufactured.) It is a Class A drug. The usual way of taking it is by sniffing it through a tube. It is much more expensive than amphetamines, but produces similar effects. Recently cocaine has become available more cheaply as 'crack'. This is cocaine mixed with baking soda. Its effects occur fairly quickly then diminish, so users tend to take repeated doses. Such a 'spree' can lead to the same effects as high doses of amphetamines, with fatigue and depression as after-effects. A strong psychological, but not physical, dependence may develop. Repeated sniffing causes physical damage to the inside of the nose.

■ Solvent abuse

Whereas cocaine snorting tended to be a habit of the rich, glue sniffing has long been available to youngsters, rich and poor. The solvents in certain glues, paints, cleaning materials, etc., release vapours which when they are inhaled, produce similar effects to alcohol or anaesthetics. Sniffers usually indulge their habit in a group, and get merry and fool about together. Accidental death or injury can happen by irresponsible behaviour when intoxicated, or by choking on vomit, or by suffocating in the plastic inhaling bag. Sniffing produces hangover symptoms but not serious physical dependence. Very long-term solvent abuse can cause similar physical damage to that caused by chronic alcohol addiction.

■ Cannabis

Cannabis is a plant from which various forms of preparation are obtained, including marijuana (herbal cannabis, pot, grass), hashish resin and cannabis oil. Cannabis is generally rolled up into a cigarette, often combined with tobacco, and smoked. It can also be smoked in a pipe, put into food or made into a drink. Cannabis is an illegal drug in Class B, though many people would like to see it legalised. They claim that it produces no harmful effects other than mild intoxication and so is less dangerous than the legal drugs, e.g. alcohol and tobacco. Other people claim that recent evidence suggests that chromosomal damage, interference with sex hormone function and brain damage may be caused by cannabis derivatives.

Marijuana is usually smoked in company, when the social situation adds much to the drug's effects. It promotes relaxation, talkativeness and heightened perception of sound and colour. The effects start quickly and last for several hours. Cannabis does not seem to produce physical dependence, though regular users develop a psychological dependence upon its 'social lubricant' effect. As with other sedating drugs, chronic intoxication causes people to become apathetic to external events and personal ambition. It is difficult to identify cause and effect in this situation.

■ LSD

LSD (lysergic acid diethylamide) is a synthetic white powder which is packaged as tiny coloured tablets, or as spots on gelatine or paper stamps. It is taken by mouth. LSD and other hallucinogenic drugs are Class A substances. The effects of one dose are quite long-lasting. Depending on the dose, a 'trip' starts about an hour after taking LSD, it peaks after about six hours and fades after about twelve hours. Intensified perceptions, heightened self-awareness and mystical experiences are more common than true hallucinations. 'Bad trips' including depression, dizziness and panic may occur. Deaths by suicide or accidents resulting from such experiences, though much publicised, are rare. Tolerance rapidly develops but physical dependence does not. Repeated use may cause psychological disturbances particularly in people with existing psychological problems.

■ Magic mushrooms

There are several species of wild mushroom which produce hallucinogenic effects when eaten. It is not illegal to possess these plants but it is illegal to prepare a product containing the hallucinogenic agent from them. The effects are similar to those of LSD. The major hazard in indulging in magic mushrooms is the risk of misidentification and subsequent poisoning by lethal species of fungi.

■ Ecstasy

Ecstasy consists of a substance called MDMA (3,4 methylenedioxymethamphetamine). It is classed as a hallucinogenic amphetamine since its effects combine those of amphetamine and LSD. Similar compounds are derived from natural products such as parsley and saffron but MDMA is produced synthetically. It was originally developed in the hope of medical applications but its widespread recreational use caused it to be banned in the USA in 1985. In Britain, MDMA is a Class A drug; penalties for possession or dealing are respectively up to seven years or up to life in prison plus an unlimited fine.

Ecstasy is usually supplied impregnated into small brightly-coloured discs of paper. Its use is associated with clubs and parties where 'Acid House' music is enjoyed.

The effects of moderate doses of MDMA are similar to other amphetamines, stimulating the heart and breathing rate and lessening the appetite. A rush of euphoria, followed by feelings of calmness and heightened perception are experienced. The alleged aphrodisiac properties are over-rated; it tends to inhibit erection and orgasm. High doses can induce hallucinations and prolonged use may cause anxiety, confusion and insomnia. Tolerance develops to the effects of MDMA but there is no physical dependence or long term compulsive use.

Most dangers of Ecstasy arise if the supply is not pure MDMA. There are many more potent compounds chemically similar to MDMA. Some have extremely powerful LSD-like effects and some are lethal even in moderate doses. Mixtures of these drugs are made illegally in amateur laboratories and are offered for sale as Ecstasy with potentially lethal consequences.

Q 12. Smoking conventional nicotine cigarettes has been shown conclusively to cause fatal diseases in many, but not all, smokers. Smoking pot has not yet been shown to have such harmful outcomes. Discuss why the former activity is legal and the latter illegal.

13. There is much controversy about the advertising of cigarettes and about the sponsorship of sporting and artistic events by tobacco companies. Discuss with your colleagues the issues involved and your opinions on these matters.

FURTHER QUESTIONS

A number of questions have been asked in the text of this book and most of them are the type that are set as part of an advanced examination. Some questions that have actually appeared in recent examinations now follow.

1. Patterns of contraceptive practices vary widely between different countries in the world. There is wide variation also in the total fertility rate (TFR). Total fertility rate is the number of children an average woman would have if current fertility patterns were to continue.

The table below gives information on the percentage use of contraceptive practices and the total fertility rate (TFR) among married women aged 15-44 in 10 countries.

Discuss the significance of this information in relation to variation in contraceptive practices. In your answer you may wish to refer to other factors such as possible social attitudes and conditions together with changes in world population.

Country	Percentage use of contraceptive practices										Total fertility rate (TFR)
	All methods combined	Female voluntary sterilisation	Male voluntary sterilisation	Oral contraceptive	I.U.D.	Condoms	Vaginal methods	Rhythm	Withdrawal	Other	
UK	77	8	8	28	7	18	2	1	5	0	1.8
Finland	80	4	1	10	29	32	1	1	2	0	1.6
Romania	60	1	0	1	1	3	1	24	26	3	2.4
Bulgaria	76	1	1	2	2	2	0	4	60	4	2.1
USA	68	17	10	13	5	10	7	3	1	2	1.8
Costa Rica	66	16	1	22	6	9	1	6	3	2	3.5
Thailand	59	19	4	20	4	2	0	1	2	7	3.8
Republic of Korea	37	2	3	9	9	6	0	5	3	0	2.5
Jordan	26	3	0	8	9	1	1	2	2	0	6.5
Nepal	7	2	3	1	0	0	0	0	0	1	5.8

(London, Human Biology, S, 1992)

2. (a) State two ways in which the skeleton (excluding the skull) of *Homo habilis* differs from that of *Homo sapiens*. (2)

(b) State three visible differences shown by the skulls of the two subspecies shown below. (3)

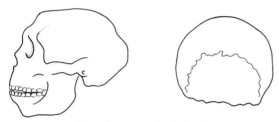
H. sapiens neanderthalensis

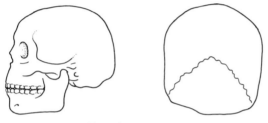
H. sapiens sapiens

(c) Describe one method by which fossilised skeletons can be dated. (2)

(d) The earliest stone tools of hominids were pebbles, usually from river gravels. Many of these had not been shaped in any way. Suggest how such pebbles may be identified as tools. (1)

(*London, Human Biology, AS, 1992*)

3. Sickle-cell anaemia is an autosomal recessive genetic defect. The diagram shows the pedigree of a family affected by sickle-cell anaemia.

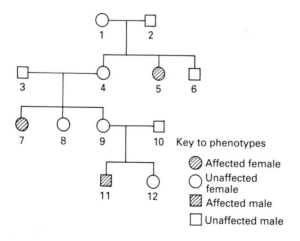

Key to phenotypes

⊘ Affected female
◯ Unaffected female
▨ Affected male
☐ Unaffected male

(a) State the numbers of all the individuals in the pedigree that are certain to be heterozygous for this gene. (3)

(b) What is the probability that individual 6 is heterozygous for this gene? (1)

(c) The parasite which causes malaria digests haemoglobin in the red blood cells (erythrocytes). Suggest why individuals heterozygous for this gene may show increased resistance to malaria. (2)

(*London, Human Biology, AS, 1992*)

4. The graph below shows a demographic transition which took place in a country.

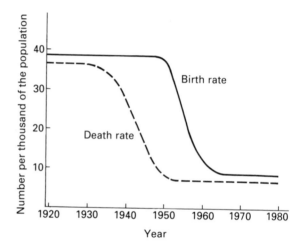

The chart below shows the age composition of countries A, B and C.

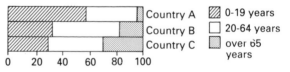

Country A   ▨ 0-19 years
Country B   ☐ 20-64 years
Country C   ▩ over 65 years

(a) (i) Describe in detail the changes in birth rate from 1920 to 1980. (2)
(ii) What was the population growth in 1950? (1)
(iii) Suggest reasons for the changes in birth rate and death rate during the years 1940-1960. (2)

(b) (i) Which of the countries in the chart has the greatest potential for population increase? (1)
(ii) Suggest a factor which may prevent such a population increase. (1)

(*Scotland, Higher Grade, Specimen 1992*)

INDEX